Taking An ASE Certification Test

This study guide will help prepare you to take and pass the ASE test. It contains descriptions of the types of questions used on the test, the task list from which the test questions are derived, a review of the task list subject information, and a practice test containing ASE style questions.

ABOUT ASE

The National Institute for Automotive Service Excellence (ASE) is a non-profit organization founded in 1972 for the purpose of improving the quality of automotive service and repair through the voluntary testing and certification of automotive technicians. Currently, there are over 400,000 professional technicians certified by ASE in over 40 different specialist areas.

ASE certification recognizes your knowledge and experience, and since it is voluntary, taking and passing an ASE certification test also demonstrates to employers and customers your commitment to your profession. It can mean better compensation and increased employment opportunities as well.

ASE not only certifies technician competency, it also promotes the benefits of technician certification to the motoring public. Repair shops that employ at least one ASE technician can display the ASE sign. Establishments where 75 percent of technicians are certified, with at least one technician certified

in each area of service offered by the business, are eligible for the ASE Blue Seal of Excellence program. ASE encourages consumers to patronize these shops through media campaigns and car care clinics.

To become ASE certified, you must pass at least one ASE exam and have at least two years of related work experience. Technicians that pass specified tests in a series earn Master Technician status. Your certification is valid for five years, after which time you must retest to retain certification, demonstrating that you have kept up with the changing technology in the field.

THE ASE TEST

An ASE test consists of forty to eighty multiple-choice questions. Test questions are written by a panel of technical experts from vehicle, parts and equipment manufacturers, as well as working technicians and technical education instructors. All questions have been pre-tested and quality checked on a national sample of technicians. The questions are derived from information presented in the task list, which details the knowledge that

a technician must have to pass an ASE test and be recognized as competent in that category. The task list is periodically updated by ASE in response to changes in vehicle technology and repair techniques.

There are five types of questions on an ASE test:
- **Direct, or Completion**
- **MOST Likely**
- **Technician A and Technician B**
- **EXCEPT**
- **LEAST Likely**

Direct, or Completion

This type of question is the kind that is most familiar to anyone who has taken a multiple-choice test: you must answer a direct question or complete a statement with the correct answer. There are four choices given as potential answers, but only one is correct. Sometimes the correct answer to one of these questions is clear, however in other cases more than one answer may seem to be correct. In that case, read the question carefully and choose the answer that is most correct. Here is an example of this type of test question:

A compression test shows that one cylinder is too low. A leakage test on that cylinder shows that there is excessive leakage. During the test, air could be heard coming from the tailpipe. Which of the following could be the cause?

A. broken piston rings
B. bad head gasket
C. bad exhaust gasket
D. an exhaust valve not seating

There is only one correct answer to this question, answer D. If an exhaust valve is not seated, air will leak from the combustion chamber by way of the valve out to the tailpipe and make an audible sound. Answer C is wrong because an exhaust gasket has nothing to do with combustion chamber sealing. Answers A and B are wrong because broken rings or a bad head gasket would have air leaking through the oil filler or coolant system.

MOST Likely

This type of question is similar to a direct question but it can be more challenging because all or some of the answers may be nearly correct. However, only one answer is the most correct. For example:

When a cylinder head with an overhead camshaft is discovered to be warped, which of the following is the most correct repair option?
A. replace the head
B. check for cracks, straighten the head, surface the head
C. surface the head, then straighten it
D. straighten the head, surface the head, check for cracks

The most correct answer is B. It makes no sense to perform repairs on a cylinder head that might not be usable. The head should first be checked for warpage and cracks. Therefore, answer B is more correct than answer D. The head could certainly be replaced, but the cost factor may be prohibitive and availability may be limited, so answer B is more correct than answer A. If the top of the head is warped enough to interfere with cam bore alignment and/or restrict free movement of the camshaft, the head must be straightened before it is resurfaced, so answer C is wrong.

Technician A and Technician B

These questions are the kind most commonly associated with the ASE test. With these questions you are asked to choose which technician statement is correct, or whether they both are correct or incorrect. This type of question can be difficult because very often you may find one technician's statement to be clearly correct or incorrect while the other may not be so obvious. Do you choose one technician or both? The key to answering these questions is to carefully examine each technician's statement independently and judge it on its own merit. Here is an example of this type of question:

A vehicle equipped with rack-and-pinion steering is having the front end inspected. Technician A says that the inner tie rod ends should be inspected while in their normal running position. Technician B says that if movement is felt between the tie rod stud and the socket while the tire is moved in and out, the inner tie rod should be replaced. Who is correct?
A. Technician A
B. Technician B
C. Both A and B
D. Neither A or B

The correct answer is C; both technicians' statements are correct. Technician B is clearly correct because any play felt between the tie-rod stud and the socket while the tire is moved in and out indicates that the assembly is worn and requires replacement. However, Technician A is also correct because inner tie- rods should be inspected while in their normal running position, to prevent binding that may occur when the suspension is allowed to hang free.

EXCEPT

This kind of question is sometimes called a negative question because you are asked to give the incorrect answer. All of the possible answers given are correct EXCEPT one. In effect, the correct answer to the question is the one that is wrong. The word EXCEPT is always capitalized in these questions. For example:

All of the following are true of torsion bars **EXCEPT**:
A. They can be mounted longitudinally or transversely.
B. They serve the same function as coil springs.
C. They are interchangeable from side-to-side
D. They can be used to adjust vehicle ride height.

The correct answer is C. Torsion bars are not normally interchangeable from side-to-side. This is because the direction of the twisting or torsion is not the same on the left and right sides. All of the other answers contain true statements regarding torsion bars.

LEAST Likely

This type of question is similar to EXCEPT in that once again you are asked to give the answer that is wrong. For example:

Blue-gray smoke comes from the exhaust of a vehicle during deceleration. Of the following, which cause is **LEAST** likely?
A. worn valve guides
B. broken valve seals
C. worn piston rings
D. clogged oil return passages

The correct answer is C. Worn piston rings will usually make an engine smoke worse under acceleration. All of the other causes can allow oil to be drawn through the valve guides under the high intake vacuum that occurs during deceleration.

PREPARING FOR THE ASE TEST

Begin preparing for the test by reading the task list. The task list describes the actual work performed by a technician in a particular specialty area. Each question on an ASE test is derived from a task or set of tasks in the list. Familiarizing yourself with the task list will help you to concentrate on the areas where you need to study.

The text section of this study guide contains information pertaining to each of the tasks in the task list. Reviewing this information will prepare you to take the practice test.

Take the practice test and compare your answers with the correct answer explanations. If you get an answer wrong and don't understand why, go back and read the information pertaining to that question in the text.

After reviewing the tasks and the subject information and taking the practice test, you should be prepared to take the ASE test or be aware of areas where further study is needed. When studying with this study guide or any other source of information, use the following guidelines to make sure the time spent is as productive as possible:

- Concentrate on the subject areas where you are weakest.
- Arrange your schedule to allow specific times for studying.
- Study in an area where you will not be distracted.
- Don't try to study after a full meal or when you are tired.
- Don't wait until the last minute and try to 'cram' for the test.

REGISTERING FOR ASE COMPUTER-BASED TESTING

Registration for the ASE CBT tests can be done online in myASE or over the phone. While not mandatory, it is recommended that you establish a myASE account on the ASE website (www.ase.com). This can be a big help in managing the ASE certification process, as your test scores and certification expiry dates are all listed there.

Test times are available during two-month windows with a one-month break in between. This means that there is a total of eight months over the period of the calendar year that ASE testing is available.

Testing can be scheduled during the daytime, night, and weekends for maximum flexibility. Also, results are available immediately after test completion. Printed certificates are mailed at the end of the two-month test window. If you fail a test, you will not be allowed to register for the same test until the next two-month test window.

TAKING THE ASE TEST – COMPUTER-BASED TESTING (CBT)

On test day, bring some form of photo identification with you and be sure to arrive at the test center 30 minutes early to give sufficient time to check in. Once you have checked in, the test supervisor will issue you some scratch paper and pencils, as well as a composite vehicle test booklet if you are taking advanced tests. You will then be seated at a computer station and given a short online tutorial on how to complete the ASE CBT tests. You may skip the tutorial if you are already familiar with the CBT process.

The test question format is similar to those found in written ASE tests. Regular certification tests have a time limit of 1 to 2 hours, depending on the test. Recertification tests are 30 to 45 minutes, and the L1 and L2 advanced level tests are capped at 2 hours. The time remaining for your test is displayed on the top left of the test window. You are given a warning when you have 5 minutes left to complete the test.

Read through each question carefully. If you don't know the answer to a question and need to think about it, click on the "Flag" button and move on to the next question. You may also go back to previous questions by pressing the "Previous Question" button. Don't spend too much time on any one question. After you have worked through to the end of the test, check your remaining time and go back and answer the questions you flagged. Very often, information found in questions later in the test can help answer some of the ones with which you had difficulty.

Some questions may have more content than what can fit on one screen. If this is the case, there will be a "More" button displayed where the "Next Question" button would ordinarily appear. A scrolling bar will also appear, showing what part of the question you are currently viewing. Once you have viewed all of the related content for the question, the "Next Question" button will reappear.

You can change answers on any of the questions before submitting the test for scoring. At the end of the examination, you will be shown a table with all of the question numbers. This table will show which questions are answered, which are unanswered, and which have been flagged for review. You will be given the option to review all the questions, review the flagged questions, or review the unanswered questions from this page. This table can be reviewed at any time during the exam by clicking the "Review" button.

If you are running out of time and still have unanswered test questions, guess the answers if necessary to make sure every question is answered. Do not leave any answers blank. It is to your advantage to answer every question, because your test score is based on the number of correct answers. A guessed answer could be correct, but a blank answer can never be.

Once you are satisfied that all of the questions are complete and ready for scoring, click the "Submit for Scoring" button. If you are scheduled for more than one test, the next test will begin immediately. If you are done with testing, you will be asked to complete a short survey regarding the CBT test experience. As you are leaving the test center, your supervisor will give you a copy of your test results. Your scores will also be available on myASE within two business days.

To learn exactly where and when the ASE Certification Tests are available in your area, as well as the costs involved in becoming ASE certified, please contact ASE directly for registration information.

The National Institute for Automotive Service Excellence
101 Blue Seal Drive, S.E. Suite 101
Leesburg, VA 20175
1-800-390-6789
http://www.ase.com

Table of Contents
A8 - Engine Performance

The Building Blocks of Our Success

At Federated Auto Parts, you know you will always get great service and support from the most knowledgeable people in the business. You also know that you will get the best brand name, premium quality auto parts available. Parts that you can trust will help you get the job done right.

Engine Performance
TEST SPECIFICATIONS
FOR ENGINE PERFORMANCE (TEST A8)

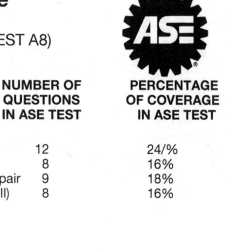

CONTENT AREA	NUMBER OF QUESTIONS IN ASE TEST	PERCENTAGE OF COVERAGE IN ASE TEST
A. General Diagnosis	12	24/%
B. Ignition System Diagnosis And Repair	8	16%
C. Fuel, Air Induction And Exhaust Systems Diagnosis And Repair	9	18%
D. Emissions Control Systems Diagnosis And Repair (Including ODB II)	8	16%
1. Positive Crankcase Ventilation (1)		
2. Exhaust Gas Recirculation (2)		
3. Secondary Air Injection (AIR) And Catalytic Converter (2)		
4. Evaporative Emissions Controls (3)		
E. Computerized Engine Controls Diagnosis And Repair (Including ODB II)	13	26%
Total	**50**	**100%**

There could be up to 10 additional questions that are included for statistical research purposes only. Your answers to these questions will not affect your test score, but since you do not know which ones they are, you should answer all questions in the test. The 5-year Recertification Test will cover the same content areas as those listed above. However, the number of questions in each content area of the Recertification Test will be reduced by about one-half.

The following pages list the tasks covered in each content area. These task descriptions offer detailed information to technicians preparing for the test, and to persons who are instructing Engine Performance technicians. The task list may also serve as a guideline for question writers, reviewers and test assemblers.

It should be noted that the number of questions in each content area might not equal the number of tasks listed. Some of the tasks are complex and broad in scope, and may be covered by several questions. Other tasks are simple and narrow in scope; one question may cover several tasks. The main purpose for listing the tasks is to describe accurately what is done on the job, not to make each task correspond to a particular test question.

ENGINE PERFORMANCE TEST TASK LIST

A. GENERAL DIAGNOSIS
(12 questions)

Task 1 - Verify driver's complaint, perform visual inspection and/or road test vehicle; determine needed action.

Task 2 - Research applicable vehicle and service information, such as engine management system operation, vehicle service history, service precautions, technical service bulletins and service campaigns/recalls.

Task 3 - Diagnose noises and/or vibration problems related to engine performance; determine needed action.

Task 4 - Diagnose the cause of un-usual exhaust color, odor and sound; determine needed action.

Task 5 - Perform engine manifold vacuum or pressure tests; determine needed action.

Task 6 - Perform cylinder power balance test; determine needed action.

Task 7 - Perform cylinder cranking compression test; determine needed action.

Task 8 - Perform cylinder leakage/leak-down test; determine needed action.

Task 9 - Diagnose engine mechanical, electrical, electronic, fuel and ignition problems with an oscilloscope, engine analyzer and/or scan tool; determine needed action.

Task 10 - Prepare and inspect vehicle for HC, CO, CO_2 and O_2 exhaust gas analysis; perform test and interpret exhaust gas readings.

Task 11 - Verify valve adjustment on engines with mechanical or hydraulic lifters.

Task 12 - Verify camshaft timing (including engines equipped with variable valve timing); determine needed action.

Task 13 - Verify engine operating temperature, check coolant level and condition, perform cooling system pressure test; determine needed repairs.

Task 14 - Inspect and test mechanical/electrical fans, fan clutch, fan shroud/ducting and fan control devices; determine needed repairs.

Task 15 - Read and interpret electrical schematic diagrams and symbols.

Task 16 - Test and diagnose emissions or driveability problems caused by battery condition, connections or excessive key-off battery drain; determine needed repairs.

Task 17 - Perform starter current draw test; determine needed action.

Task 18 - Perform starter circuit voltage drop tests; determine needed action.

Task 19 - Inspect, test and repair or replace components and wires in the starter control circuit.

Task 20 - Test and diagnose engine performance problems resulting from an undercharge, overcharge or a no-charge condition; determine needed action.

Task 21 - Inspect, adjust and replace alternator (generator) drive belts, pulleys, tensioners and fans.

Task 22 - Inspect, test and repair or replace charging circuit components, connectors and wires.

B. IGNITION SYSTEM DIAGNOSIS AND REPAIR
(8 questions)

Task 1 - Diagnose ignition system related problems such as no-starting, hard starting, engine misfire, poor driveability, spark knock, power loss, poor mileage and emissions problems; determine root cause; determine needed repairs.

Task 2 - Interpret ignition system related diagnostic trouble codes (DTCs); determine needed repairs.

Task 3 - Inspect, test, repair or replace ignition primary circuit wiring and components.

Task 4 - Inspect, test, service, repair or replace ignition system secondary circuit wiring and components.

Task 5 - Inspect, test and replace ignition coil(s).

Task 6 - Inspect, test and replace ignition system sensors; adjust as necessary.

Task 7 - Inspect, test and/or replace ignition control module (ICM)/powertrain/engine control module (PCM/ECM); reprogram as needed.

C. FUEL, AIR INDUCTION AND EXHAUST SYSTEMS DIAGNOSIS AND REPAIR
(9 questions)

Task 1 - Diagnose fuel system related problems, including hot or cold no-starting, hard starting, poor driveability, incorrect idle speed, poor idle, flooding, hesitation, surging, engine misfire, power loss, stalling, poor mileage and emissions problems; determine root cause; determine needed action.

Task 2 - Interpret fuel or induction system related diagnostic trouble codes (DTCs); analyze fuel trim and other scan tool data; determine needed repairs.

Task 3 - Inspect fuel tank, filler neck and gas cap; inspect and replace fuel lines, fittings and hoses; check fuel for contaminants and quality.

Task 4 - Inspect, test and replace fuel pump(s) and/or fuel pump assembly; inspect, service and replace fuel filters.

Task 5 - Inspect and test electric fuel pump control circuits and components; determine needed repairs.

Task 6 - Inspect, test and repair or replace fuel pressure regulation system and components of fuel injection systems; perform fuel pressure/volume test.

Task 7 - Inspect, remove, service or replace throttle assembly; make related adjustments.

Task 8 - Inspect, test, clean and replace fuel injectors and fuel rails.

Task 9 - Inspect, service and repair or replace air filtration system components.

Task 10 - Inspect throttle assembly, air induction system, intake manifold and gaskets for air/vacuum leaks and/or unmetered air.

Task 11 - Remove, clean, inspect, test and repair or replace fuel system vacuum and electrical components and connections.

Task 12 - Inspect, service and replace exhaust manifold, exhaust pipes, oxygen sensors, mufflers, catalytic converters, resonators, tailpipes and heat shields.

Task 13 - Test for exhaust system restriction or leaks; determine needed action.

Task 14 - Inspect, test, clean and repair or replace turbocharger or supercharger and system components.

D. EMISSIONS CONTROL SYSTEMS DIAGNOSIS AND REPAIR (INCLUDING OBD II)
(8 questions)

1. POSITIVE CRANKCASE VENTILATION
(1 question)

Task 1 - Test and diagnose emissions or driveability problems caused by positive crankcase ventilation (PCV) system.

Task 2 - Inspect, service and replace positive crankcase ventilation (PCV) filter/breather cap, valve, tubes, orifice/metering device and hoses.

2. EXHAUST GAS RECIRCULATION
(2 questions)

Task 1 - Test and diagnose driveability problems caused by the exhaust gas recirculation (EGR) system.

Task 2 - Interpret exhaust gas recirculation (EGR) related scan tool data and diagnostic trouble codes (DTCs); determine needed repairs.

Task 3 - Inspect, test, service and replace components of the EGR system, including EGR valve, tubing, passages, vacuum/pressure controls, filters, hoses, electrical/electronic sensors, controls, solenoids and wiring of exhaust gas recirculation (EGR) systems.

3. SECONDARY AIR INJECTION (AIR) AND CATALYTIC CONVERTER
(2 questions)

Task 1 - Test and diagnose emissions or driveability problems caused by the secondary air injection or catalytic converter systems.

Task 2 - Interpret secondary air injection system related scan tool data and diagnostic trouble codes (DTCs); determine needed repairs.

Task 3 - Inspect, test, service and replace mechanical components and electrical/electronically-operated components and circuits of secondary air injection systems.

Task 4 - Inspect catalytic converter. Interpret catalytic converter related diagnostic trouble codes (DTCs); analyze related scan tool data to determine root cause of DTCs; determine needed repairs.

4. EVAPORATIVE EMISSIONS CONTROLS
(3 questions)

Task 1 - Test and diagnose emissions or driveability problems caused by the evaporative emissions control system.

Task 2 - Interpret evaporative emissions related scan tool data and diagnostic trouble codes (DTCs); determine needed repairs.

Task 3 - Inspect, test and replace canister, lines/hoses, mechanical and electrical components of the evaporative emissions control system.

E. COMPUTERIZED ENGINE CONTROLS DIAGNOSIS AND REPAIR (INCLUDING OBD II)
(13 questions)

Task 1 - Retrieve and record diagnostic trouble codes (DTCs), OBD II monitor status and freeze frame data.

Task 2 - Diagnose the causes of emissions or driveability problems with stored or active diagnostic trouble codes (DTCs).

Task 3 - Diagnose the causes of emissions or driveability problems without diagnostic trouble codes (DTCs).

Task 4 - Use a scan tool, digital multimeter (DMM) or digital storage oscilloscope (DSO) to inspect or test computerized engine control system sensors, actuators, circuits and powertrain/engine control module (PCM/ECM); determine needed repairs.

Task 5 - Measure and interpret voltage, voltage drop, amperage and resistance using digital multimeter (DMM) readings.

Task 6 - Test, remove, inspect, clean, service and repair or replace power and ground distribution circuits and connections.

Task 7 - Remove and replace the powertrain/engine control module (PCM/ECM); reprogram as needed.

Task 8 - Diagnose driveability and emissions problems resulting from failures of interrelated systems (for example: cruise control, security alarms/theft deterrent, torque controls, traction controls, torque management, A/C, non-OEM installed accessories).

Task 9 - Clear diagnostic trouble codes (DTCs), run all OBD II monitors and verify the repair.

The preceding Task List Data details all of the relevant subject matter you are expected to know in order to sit for this ASE Certification Test. Your own years of experience as a professional technician in the automotive service industry should provide you with additional background.

Finally, a conscientious review of the self-study material provided in this Training for ASE Certification unit will help you to be adequately prepared to take this test.

General Diagnosis

Proper engine performance, emissions levels that are within allowances and good fuel economy all depend upon a quality, well-timed spark, fuel, air and compression. No matter how sophisticated the engine and its controls become, they will still rely upon these four basic components.

When engine performance problems occur, such as no-starting, hard-starting, poor fuel economy or loss of power, diagnosis should be performed in a logical manner, using a process of elimination. Begin by questioning the driver about the vehicle's symptoms, when they occur, and how long they have been occurring. What does the customer have to do to experience the problem? Is there a temperature, running time, time spent without running, speed, or road condition prerequisite?

Always perform a road test, if possible, to verify the driver's complaint. But before road testing, perform a visual inspection under the hood to check for obvious problems. Check the accessory drive belt(s) for looseness, cracks, glazing or fraying. A loose alternator belt could be the cause of a charging system problem. Check the battery cables and all electrical wires and connections for damage and secure connections. Quite often a problem in a computerized engine control system circuit is not caused by a component but rather by broken or abraded wires or corroded connectors. Check the condition and routing of all vacuum lines. Broken or disconnected vacuum hoses can cause an engine to run roughly or stall.

Check the vehicle's service history to look for similar complaints in the past. Check for TSBs (Technical Service Bulletins) that may reveal updated repair information regarding the symptoms or system in question. Doing research at this point could save valuable time that would otherwise be needlessly spent trying to achieve a diagnosis. Check for recalls and service campaigns, which may indicate that the problem is in fact a defect that the vehicle manufacturer will correct. Some investigation here could save your customer from unnecessarily paying for a repair.

If the initial inspection and road test reveal that there is an engine performance problem, vacuum, compression, cylinder leakage and cylinder balance tests can be performed to make sure the engine is mechanically in good condition.

We employ technicians certified by the
National Institute for

**AUTOMOTIVE
SERVICE
EXCELLENCE**

Let us show you their credentials

ENGINE NOISES

Start the engine and let it idle while listening for unusual noises. Generally, noises are caused by too much clearance between parts or loss of oil pressure. The following common engine noises can be caused by any of these parts:

Crankshaft Noises
- Main bearings
- Connecting rod bearings
- Pistons
- Wrist pin
- Crankshaft end-play

Valvetrain Noises
- Bearing noise
- Rocker arms, shaft, ball and seat
- Pushrods
- Tappets and camshaft
- Timing gears and chain

Other Noises
- Loose or broken brackets
- Oil pump failure
- Spark knock.

In order to successfully diagnose noises, you must pay close attention to the frequency at which the noise occurs and how the frequency changes as you vary engine load and engine rpm. Also note how factors such as temperature and oil pressure affect the noise. A stethoscope can be used to find the location of a noise.

Bearing Noises

Main bearing noise is caused by too much bearing clearance due to worn bearings or crankshaft journals or a lack of lubrication. It is usually indicated by a dull or deep-sounding metallic knocking. When you increase rpm or engine load, the knocking usually increases in frequency. The noise is usually most obvious right after the engine starts up, when the engine is under a heavy load, or during acceleration. Along with the knocking sound, the engine may also exhibit low oil pressure.

Connecting rod noise, which is also caused by excessive bearing clearance or lack of lubrication, is much less intense than main bearing noise. This noise usually sounds like a light metallic rapping that is most noticeable when the engine is running under a light load at relatively slow speeds. This knock becomes louder and occurs more frequently when the speed of the engine is increased. When you eliminate the ignition or injection to the cylinder with a rod knock, the sound diminishes.

Crankshaft End-Play Noise

Crankshaft end-play noise occurs when there is excessive clearance between the crankshaft thrust bearing and the machined faces of the crankshaft thrust journal, allowing the crankshaft to move back and forth.

When crankshaft end-play is excessive, the engine may make a deep knocking sound that is usually most obvious at idle but diminishes when a load is placed on the crankshaft, such as when the clutch is disengaged on a manual transmission vehicle.

Where space allows, you can verify excessive crankshaft end-play by fitting a dial indicator to the tip of the crankshaft. Using a prybar, carefully pry the crankshaft back and forth and note the reading on the dial indicator. Compare the reading with specifications.

Piston Noise

Excessive piston-to-wall clearance can cause piston slap. This is caused by side-to-side movement of the piston within the cylinder bore, and sounds like a dull or muffled metallic rattle at idle or during light engine loads.

Very faint piston slap may disappear after the engine warms up and the piston expands. In this case, the piston-to-wall clearance usually isn't severe enough to worry about. However, piston slap that continues after the engine warms up should be corrected. Note that unlike a connecting rod bearing noise, piston slap does not quiet down and may in fact grow louder when you eliminate ignition or fuel injection to that cylinder.

A knocking noise can be caused by excessive carbon buildup in the combustion chamber where the piston contacts the carbon at TDC.

Piston Pin Noise

When piston-to-piston pin clearance is excessive, the pin makes a light but sharp metallic rapping at idle. The sound may be more obvious during low-speed driving. Eliminating ignition or fuel injection to a cylinder with a loose piston pin will change the frequency and possibly the intensity of the rapping noise.

Valvetrain Noise

Valvetrain noise can be caused by excessive valve clearance in adjustable valvetrains, worn components like rocker arms, shafts, lifters and camshaft, or lack of lubrication. It is usually indicated by a light ticking noise at idle that occurs at a frequency slower than engine rpm. This is because the valvetrain operates at half the crankshaft speed.

Hydraulic Lifters

A noisy hydraulic lifter usually makes a consistent ticking sound. Try sliding a feeler gauge between the valve stem and the rocker arm. If this eliminates the ticking, it confirms that there is excessive clearance in the valvetrain.

With the engine running, you can also press down on the pushrod end of each rocker arm with a piece of wood or a hammer handle. If this stops or reduces the ticking, you have pinpointed the faulty lifter. Always check valve adjustment and inspect valvetrain parts for wear or damage. Worn valvetrain parts can mimic the noise of bad hydraulic lifters.

Spark Knock

Spark knock, which is caused by two kinds of abnormal, uncontrolled combustion, sounds like a metallic pinging or ringing noise. You may hear spark knock when the engine is under a heavy load and being run at too low an rpm, or when the engine is accelerating. An engine that is running too hot and/or has excessive combustion deposits can also suffer from spark knock.

Preignition spark knock occurs when a hot piece of carbon or metal inside the combustion chamber prematurely ignites the air/fuel mixture. Then the spark plug ignites the remaining mixture at the normal time. When the two portions of burning mixture meet each other inside the combustion chamber, there is a sudden and abnormal rise in cylinder pressure, which causes engine vibration in that cylinder.

Detonation spark knock is primarily caused by fuel with too low an octane rating for the engine, ignition timing that is too far advanced, high engine operating temperature or excessive carbon buildup in the combustion chamber. If the octane rating is too low for the engine, it basically means that the fuel will burn too quickly. When detonation occurs, the spark fires, the mixture begins burning, and pressure in the cylinder begins rising. But the rise in normal pressure causes part of the air/fuel mixture elsewhere in the combustion chamber to self-ignite. Then the two flame fronts collide as in the preignition situation.

Both preignition and detonation can cause damage to pistons and spark plugs.

Most vehicles have a knock sensor to adjust timing as needed to avoid damage however, excessive spark knock may be a sign of engine control system problems. EGR (Exhaust Gas Recirculation) operation, knock control, coolant level, or any number of engine sensors or solenoids can cause spark knock. Asking the customer how long the engine has made this noise is the best way to determine how much damage may have occurred.

Other Noises

A high pitched squealing noise when the engine is accelerated indicates a loose or glazed drive belt.

A thumping noise at the back of the engine that is most noticeable when the vehicle is in Park or Neutral can be caused by loose torque converter bolts or a loose or cracked flexplate.

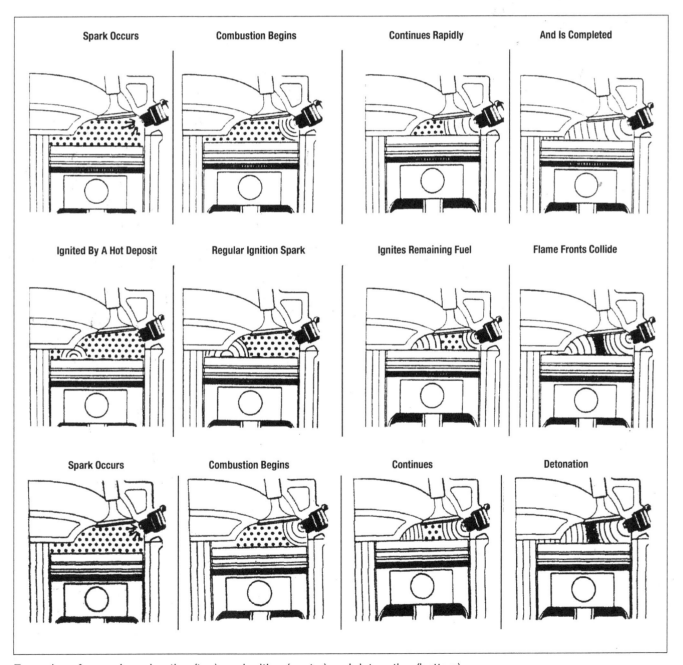

Examples of normal combustion (top), preignition (center) and detonation (bottom).

DIAGNOSING EXHAUST COLOR, ODOR AND SOUND

Black exhaust smoke indicates that the air/fuel mixture is too rich. Black smoke can be caused by a restricted air intake, leaking fuel pressure regulator diaphragm, defective fuel injector or electronic sensor misleading the computer to add more fuel than is needed. It is rare that black smoke is engine mechanical-related. The exhaust will also have a definite odor if the mixture is too rich and vehicles with catalytic converters may have a strong sulphur smell.

Excessive white exhaust smoke usually means coolant is leaking into one or more cylinders and the engine is trying to burn off that coolant. The most common cause of white smoke is a bad head gasket. A compression test must be performed to narrow down the damaged area. Any leak from the cooling system into the intake or combustion areas can cause white smoke. This problem may be masked until it becomes severe, because the catalytic converter will super-heat the water to such a fine vapor that it may not be noticeable.

Blue-gray or gray-white smoke tells you the engine is burning oil. This could be caused by something as simple as a PCV system malfunction, however, the most common causes of burning oil are worn valve guides and/or seals, and worn piston rings and/or cylinders.

Typically, bad piston rings will make the engine smoke worse when it is accelerating — especially after it has been idling for a long time. When a vehicle suffers from worn valve guides and/or bad valve stem seals, you'll see exhaust smoke during deceleration. The high intake vacuum that occurs during deceleration draws the oil through the worn guides or seals. Remember, the catalytic converter will super-heat the oil and reduce some of the smoke that would have been seen on pre-converter models.

Before you blame either the valve guides or the valve seals, verify that all of the oil return holes are clean. If oil cannot drain freely back into the crankcase, it can accumulate in the head and be drawn by vacuum into the combustion chamber, causing exhaust smoke.

A small exhaust leak will make a whistling, hissing or popping noise. A tapping sound that may sound like a valvetrain noise can actually be caused by an exhaust leak at the exhaust manifold/ cylinder head juncture. Rattling noises can be caused by loose exhaust system heat shields, loose clamps or an exhaust pipe interfering with another component. Loose internal components in the muffler and catalytic converter can also cause a rattling noise.

ENGINE VACUUM TESTS

Cranking Vacuum Test

Properly disable the ignition and fuel systems. Connect an ammeter to the starting circuit and a vacuum gauge to the intake manifold. Crank the engine, listen to the cranking rhythm, and watch your instruments.

On a good engine, the cranking speed and cranking rhythm will sound crisp and consistent. There will be no 'pauses' or uneven

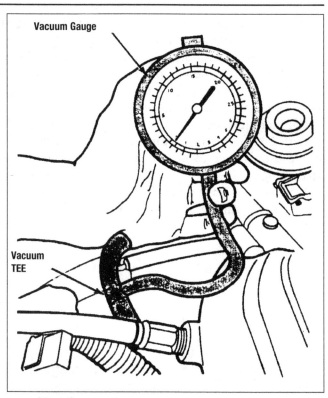

Typical vacuum gauge installed for manifold vacuum test. *(Courtesy: Ford Motor Co.)*

rhythms, suggesting binding or differing compression values. The ammeter will stabilize at a consistent current draw reading that's within specifications. The vacuum gauge will read a fairly steady 3 to 5 in. Hg or more.

The better the rings and valves are sealing, the stronger cranking vacuum will be. All things being equal, the following are true:

- The stronger the cranking vacuum, the quicker the engine will start
- The weaker the cranking vacuum, the more difficult it will be to start the engine. Moreover, if the engine can't draw any cranking vacuum at all, it won't start.

Whenever you see zero or nearly zero cranking vacuum, check for a substantial air leak such as:

- an improperly adjusted throttle blade
- a loose or cracked carburetor or intake throttle body

White needle = steady needle

Indication: Normal engine in good condition.

Gauge reading: Steady, from 17-22 in./Hg.

Indication: Late ignition or valve timing, low compression, stuck throttle valve, leaking carburetor, throttle body or intake manifold gaskets.

Gauge reading: Low (15-20 in./Hg) but steady.

Indication: Weak valve springs, worn valve stem guides or leaky cylinder head gasket (vibrating excessively at all speeds). NOTE: A plugged catalytic converter may also cause this reading.

Gauge reading: Needle fluctuates as engine speed increases.

Indication: Choked muffler or catalytic converter, or excessive back pressure in system. Choked muffler will exhibit a slow drop of vacuum to zero.

Gauge reading: Gradual drop in reading at idle. Reading decreases with rpm.

Dark needle = drifting needle

Indication: Sticking valves or ignition miss.

Gauge reading: Intermittent fluctuation at idle.

Indication: Improper carburetor adjustment or minor intake leak at carburetor or manifold. NOTE: Bad fuel injector O-rings may also cause this reading.

Gauge reading: Drifting needle.

Indication: Burnt valve or improper valve clearance. The needle will drop when the defective valve operates.

Gauge reading: Steady needle, but drops regularly.

Indication: Worn valve guides

Gauge reading: Needle vibrates excessively at idle, but steadies as engine speed increases.

Vacuum gauge readings

- a stuck-open PCV valve or a cracked PCV hose
- secondary throttle blades that are stuck open (where a carburetor is used)
- a leaking intake manifold gasket.

Zero cranking vacuum and a no-start or hard-start complaint can also be caused by a severe exhaust restriction. When in doubt, loosen the exhaust pipe(s) at the exhaust manifold(s) and repeat the test. An easier way to test quickly on many engines is to remove the oxygen sensor. Strong puffs of air from the mounting hole during cranking can indicate a restricted exhaust. A simple gauge is available to screw into the hole to measure the backpressure.

Of course, poor cranking vacuum (coupled with faster-than-normal cranking speed) could also mean that compression is low in all cylinders due to normal engine wear or due to a valve timing or timing belt problem. When timing chains or timing belts wear or stretch, valve timing can go astray. Sometimes, the camshaft drive system will literally jump a tooth and the engine will continue running (although very sluggishly).

Note that with some jumped valve timing problems, the engine will crank very unevenly and the vacuum and ammeter readings will be very erratic. You may notice that disabling the ignition on an erratically cranking engine makes the engine crank smoothly again. This indicates an ignition or valve timing problem.

Suppose the engine has one or more consistent compression leaks. Every time the cylinder with the compression leak comes around:

- the compression air volume will drop momentarily
- the cranking speed will increase momentarily
- the starter current draw will decrease momentarily.

The reason that the cranking speed increases and starter draw decreases is that it takes less effort for the starter to crank a weaker cylinder. When the cranking tests suggest a compression problem, you must perform other pinpoint tests to confirm the source of the problem. Start with compression and cylinder leakdown tests.

Manifold Vacuum Test

Checking manifold vacuum can reveal a variety of engine maladies. When the engine has reached normal operating temperature, connect a vacuum gauge to a manifold vacuum port. As a general rule, an engine in good condition should produce a steady 17 to 21 in. Hg reading at idle. However, always check the standard for the particular engine in question.

NOTE: Remember atmospheric pressure changes with elevation. Manufacturers provide sea level readings so the technician needs to adjust readings accordingly. As an approximation, for every 1000 ft. above sea level, remove one inch of vacuum.

Does the idle vacuum look OK? If so, disconnect the vacuum hose from the EGR valve and plug it. Using normal safety precautions, slowly raise engine rpm to about 2500 rpm in Neutral or Park and note the vacuum reading again.

At 2500 rpm, the vacuum reading should be equal to or greater than the idle reading. Besides making the vehicle perform very sluggishly, an exhaust restriction will cause a substantial drop in the vacuum reading at 2500 rpm.

When the idle vacuum is low but steady, suspect an air/fuel mixture that is too lean or too rich. Air leaks or vacuum leaks can cause a lean condition and are common causes of rough idle, hesitation, stalling and hard starting. If the mixture is artificially enriched by injecting propane into the induction system, an engine running lean should speed up and the vacuum reading should rise. If the air/fuel mixture is too rich, the engine will slow down and the vacuum reading will drop. If the engine is running lean and you suspect a vacuum leak as the cause, try using a propane kit with a length of hose attached to find the leak. Pass the hose end around the suspected areas and listen for a change in idle.

Worn valve guides can also cause a lean condition by allowing additional air to enter the combustion chamber. If worn valve guides are suspected, disconnect the PCV system and inject some propane into the valve cover. If the guides are at fault, the engine speed should increase and the vacuum reading should rise.

ALTITUDE	Inches Of Vacuum (in-Hg)
Sea Level to 1000 ft.	17-22
1000 ft. to 2000 ft.	16-21
2000 ft to 3000 ft.	15-20
3000 ft. to 4000 ft.	14-19
4000 ft to 5000 ft.	13-18
5000 ft to 6000 ft.	12-17

Corrected vacuum gauge readings for higher altitudes

If artificially enriching the mixture makes no difference and the engine performs sluggishly, suspect a leaking EGR valve, late ignition timing or valve timing. Note that a leaking EGR valve can cause a low but steady vacuum reading. However, it can also cause a low, somewhat unsteady reading, but not as unsteady or erratic as you see with burned or sticking valves. When in doubt, see if temporarily blocking off the EGR valve with gasket paper corrects the engine's rough idle, stalling and hesitation problems.

When the reading floats or slowly wanders above and below a normal idle reading, the carburetor is out of adjustment.

A vacuum reading that regularly drops to a much-lower-than-normal reading usually indicates leaking valves. When you see a substantial but very intermittent drop, suspect sticking valves.

With weak or broken valve springs, the vacuum reading usually flutters or oscillates at idle and when you raise engine speed.

When the reading jumps abruptly from normal to very low, it could indicate a head gasket that has blown out between two cylinders.

CYLINDER POWER BALANCE TEST

With a cylinder power balance test, you can compare the power output of all the engine's cylinders. Some technicians call it a power contribution test because it indicates how much power each cylinder contributes to the engine. The power balance test is an important technique for solving rough idle complaints.

To perform this test, let the engine idle and short out the ignition to each cylinder, one cylinder at a time. Some technicians also short cylinders at 1500 rpm and compare the results with those of the idle test. You can use an engine analyzer or a cylinder-shorting device to do this test safely. When in doubt, always refer to the manufacturer's recommended procedures for power balance tests. Many Ford products do this test during the Key On Engine Running test by turning off injectors.

Never short cylinders by pulling wires off the spark plugs. Open-circuiting a plug wire can give you a nasty shock and can damage the ignition system.

Because shorting cylinders dumps raw fuel into the catalytic converter, the converter could overheat. Allow about a 20-second cool-down period after you short each cylinder.

If each cylinder is producing about the same power, idle rpm will drop the same amount every time you short a cylinder. The cylinder(s) that show little or no rpm drop are either weak or dead. After you identify a weak cylinder or cylinders, you have to determine what those cylinders have in common with each other.

Two consecutive cylinders in firing order that are weak or dead often share an ignition problem. For example, the spark plug wires on these cylinders may be crossed. Or, there may be a carbon track or crack between their terminals inside the distributor cap. Sometimes, two problem cylinders share an ignition coil, as in a distributorless ignition system.

Two weak cylinders also could be related because they are the closest cylinders to an intake air leak or a leaking EGR valve. A somewhat centralized air leak such as a loose carburetor or throttle body housing can affect each cylinder to a different extent, resulting in erratic and unpredictable rpm drops during repeated power balance tests.

On a carbureted engine, watch out for rpm drops that are alternately high and low. When every other cylinder in firing order shows a high rpm drop, look for unbalanced idle mixture screws or a dirty idle circuit on one side of the carburetor. Remember that on a traditional intake system, each side of the carburetor feeds alternate cylinders in firing order.

A power balance test can also be conducted using an exhaust gas analyzer. This is accomplished by measuring the amount of HC (hydrocarbons) increase each time a cylinder is cancelled. A substantial increase in hydrocarbons tells you that the injector is delivering enough fuel and that the valvetrain is allowing the fuel to enter and exit the cylinder. If HC does not increase or rises only slightly when a cylinder is shorted out, then either the injector is malfunctioning or there is a problem in the valvetrain.

If you have no other obvious signs of why a cylinder is weak on the power balance test, you may have to remove the valve cover and look for valvetrain wear. Before you use any measuring tools, turn the engine over very slowly and see if valve action on the weak cylinder is the same as it is on the strong cylinders. Now, check the clearances. If a rocker shaft is used, consider the possibility of shaft wear. If there are pushrods, shine a light along the length of each one. Are there any bent pushrods? A bent pushrod can cause a weak cylinder. When two cylinders right next to each other are dead, suspect a blown head gasket or a cracked head. Follow up with a cranking compression and cylinder leakage test.

COMPRESSION TEST

Cranking Compression Test

Once you have used the power balance and cranking vacuum/

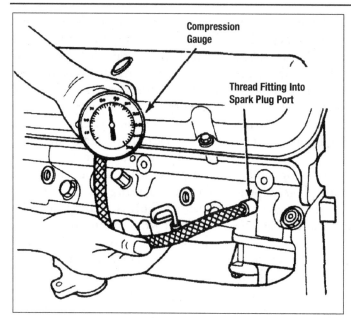

Typical engine compression tester.   *(Courtesy: Ford Motor Co.)*

cranking rhythm tests to locate a compression problem, do a compression test to determine why the cylinder is leaking compression. The two traditional ways of pinpointing a compression leak are the cranking compression test and the cylinder leakage test.

To get the most consistent and accurate results, perform a cranking compression test with the engine at normal operating temperature. Remove all of the spark plugs so the engine will crank more easily. To ensure that the engine breathes freely, remove the air cleaner and hold the throttle blade(s) wide open. Be sure the battery is strong enough to maintain the same cranking speed throughout the test. Use a battery charger if the battery is questionable.

On vehicles with distributor ignition, disconnect and isolate the positive wire at the coil. If equipped with distributorless ignition, disconnect the primary coil connector at the coil pack. Also, disable fuel injection systems so they don't spray fuel during the compression test. Disconnect the wires from the fuel pump relay or disconnect the fuel pump wire at the fuel tank.

Connect the compression gauge to the cylinder being tested, crank the engine through four compression strokes (four puffs on the compression gauge) and note how the gauge responds. Usually, cranking each cylinder through four compression strokes will give you an accurate compression reading. Pay close attention to how the gauge responds to each puff. A healthy cylinder usually builds most of its pressure on the first stroke and continues building to a good compression reading. Service manuals usually list compression pressure specifications as well as allowable deviations from them.

Wet Compression Test

During the cranking compression test, the first puff may produce weak pressure. On the second, third, and fourth puffs, the pressure may improve but never builds up to a healthy reading. When you notice this, try performing a wet compression test on that cylinder.

Squirt a spoonful of clean engine oil into the cylinder and spin the engine over to spread oil around the cylinder. Repeat the cranking compression test. If the compression improves substantially during the wet compression test, the problem may be worn compression rings, a worn piston, and/or a worn cylinder wall.

However, if the pressure is low on the first puff and remains low during a wet compression test, expect problems such as valves out of adjustment, burned valves, sticking valves, a hole in the piston, etc.

When compression is low in two adjacent cylinders, the head gasket may be blown or the block cracked between those two cylinders. Low compression on all cylinders could be a sign of worn rings on an extremely high-mileage or abused (run without enough oil) engine. It could also be an indication of valve timing that is out of specification. Compare cranking compression test results to idle vacuum readings.

CYLINDER LEAKAGE TEST

Think of the cylinder leakage test as being the last word in compression testing for a weak cylinder. In this test, you bring the piston in the weak cylinder up to TDC on the compression stroke and pump compressed air into the cylinder. Where the air leaks out shows you the location of the compression leak.

> **NOTE:** *The piston must be at TDC on the compression stroke when performing a cylinder leakage test or results will be misleading.*

A leakage tester will compare the air leaking out of the cylinder to the amount of air you are putting into it. Generally speaking, leakage greater than 20 percent indicates a problem cylinder. If you don't use a leakage tester and are testing more than one cylinder, always use the same air pressure on each cylinder.

When the air leaks out of a cylinder, it goes to one of four places. Here's how to determine where the air is going, and why:

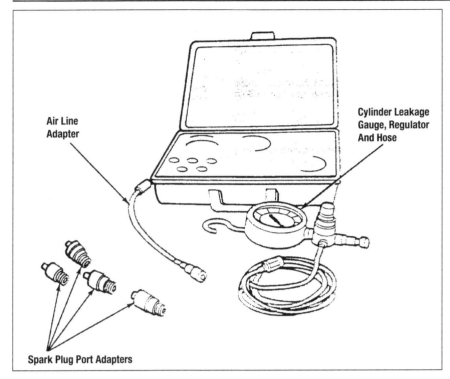

Typical cylinder leakage tester. *(Courtesy: Ford Motor Co.)*

• Air that causes bubbles in the radiator coolant indicates a cracked head, cracked block, and/or a blown head gasket
• Air that is blowing out of the carburetor or intake system confirms that an intake valve is leaking. Be sure the air you hear in the intake isn't coming from the crankcase via the PCV valve. Disconnect the PCV system and listen again
• Air that comes out of the tailpipe confirms that an exhaust valve is leaking
• Air blowing into the crankcase indicates leaking rings and/or worn pistons. To check for this type of leak, remove the engine's oil filler cap and listen.

USING A SCAN TOOL

Beginning in the late 1970's vehicle manufacturers began using electronics and on-board computers to control engine functions. On-board diagnostics were developed as a part of these systems to aid in the diagnosis of vehicle problems.

With on-board diagnostics, the engine control system's computer, known as the PCM (Powertrain Control Module) or ECM (Engine Control Module), monitors the input and output circuits in the system and compares their voltage, resistance or current values with preprogrammed parameters. If an abnormal signal is detected, a fault is stored in the PCM/ECM's memory in the form of a Diagnostic Trouble Code (DTC).

Early computerized engine control systems used a dash-mounted Malfunction Indicator Light (MIL) to communicate system status. When a fault was stored in the computer's memory, the MIL was illuminated to alert the driver and technician that there was a problem. If specific pins in a diagnostic connector were jumpered or a pigtail wire was grounded with the ignition key turned on, the MIL would then flash. Counting the flashes would reveal the code number and in turn, direct the technician to the relevant service information.

However, as engine control systems became more complex and sophisticated, a better way of communicating with the PCM/ ECM became necessary, and so the scan tool was born. The first scan tools were proprietary and designed by vehicle manufacturers for specific vehicles or systems. Aftermarket scan tools soon began to appear, but their use was complicated by the lack of standardization within the automotive industry. The location of the Data Link Connector (DLC), where the scan tool connects to the engine control system,

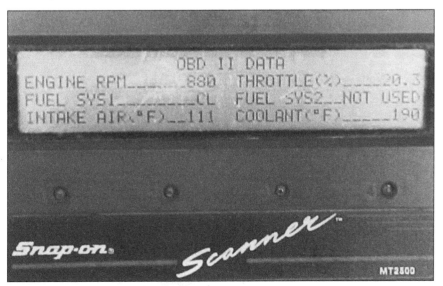

Typical scan tool screen display.

A scan tool connected to the DLC on an OBD II vehicle.

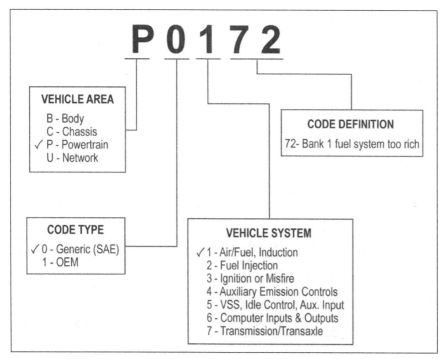

OBD II trouble code description.

ize their engine performance monitoring systems. The following regulations pertain to scan tools:

- A common scan tool can be used on all vehicle makes and models
- A scan tool must be used to retrieve OBD II DTCs
- A universal 16-pin DLC, with dedicated pin assignments
- The DLC must be located under the dash on the driver's side of the vehicle and be easily accessible
- A standard list of DTCs
- Stored DTCs must be able to be cleared from memory with a scan tool.

Before using a scan tool, read the manufacturer's instructions to become familiar with its operation. Most scan tools are equipped with removable cartridges that contain specific vehicle service information. The proper cartridge must be installed for the vehicle being serviced. To stay up to date, new cartridges must be purchased as required, although some cartridges can be updated by downloading information from a computer.

Make sure the ignition key is in the OFF position, then connect the scan tool connector to the DLC. On pre-OBD II vehicles, an adapter may have to be used. If the scan tool is not powered through the DLC, connect the power lead(s) to the cigarette lighter or battery.

The scan tool may ask you certain questions to identify the vehicle being serviced. Most scan tool have buttons or knobs with which to input information. Once the vehicle is identified, you can then select the desired diagnostic information.

DTCs are the most common requested information. Prior to OBD II, vehicle manufacturers used two and three digit codes that were proprietary to specific vehi-

varied according to manufacturer. The size of the connector and number of pins also varied, necessitating the use of adapters to connect the scan tool. The number of components monitored by the engine control system varied from manufacturer to manufacturer and each manufacturer had their own nomenclature and code numbers.

This changed when automobile manufacturers implemented On-Board Diagnostics II (OBD II) in response to Federal and the state of California emissions control system monitoring standards. OBD II requires on-board diagnostic systems to detect problems before they can result in increased emissions. In OBD II systems, components are monitored for deteriorating performance rather than just total failure.

OBD II regulations also required vehicle manufacturers to standard-

cles and systems and each manufacturer also had their own code definitions. With OBD II, common codes and definitions were developed to identify all basic emissions-related failures. OBD II trouble codes consist of one alpha character followed by four digits. The alpha character indicates the area of the vehicle where the failure occurred. This includes (B) Body, (C) Chassis, (P) Powertrain, and (U) Network. The first digit of the DTC denotes the origin of the code. Codes authored by the Society of Automotive Engineers (SAE) are identified by a zero (0). These codes are known as generic DTCs since they are the same for every vehicle. Manufacturer specific codes are indicated by the number one (1). These DTCs are part of the manufacturer's enhanced diagnostic software, and vary between brands. The second digit in the DTC identifies the system experiencing the problem, while the last two digits correspond to a specific code definition.

In addition to accessing DTCs, modern scan tools can also display datastream values. Datastream values are the electrical operating values of the sensors, actuators and circuits in the engine control system. The displayed values can then be compared with specifications in the service manual.

Some scan tools can also provide 'snapshot' data. This allows the technician to check for problems when driving the vehicle. If there is an intermittent or condition–specific problem, the technician can then take a 'snapshot' of the engine control system, capturing the various sensor readings when the malfunction occurs. The technician can then review the information back at the shop to find the cause of the problem.

Some scan tools can be used to perform tests and are known as bi-directional scan tools. The scan tool can activate various switches and actuators and then tell you whether the component is functioning properly.

USING AN OSCILLOSCOPE

An oscilloscope is an important component of an engine analyzer. It displays a graph (or waveform) of an electrical signal, and shows how that electrical signal changes over a period of time. By comparing a scope pattern to a known good pattern, a technician can determine whether something is wrong in an electrical circuit.

An oscilloscope visually displays a voltage reading on a screen in the form of a white line, or trace. Variations in voltage are shown as a waveform. There are two basic types of oscilloscopes, live analog scopes and digital storage oscilloscopes. On live analog scopes, the signal has to be repetitive or occurring at the moment of observation. A digital storage oscilloscope takes momentary samples of signals and stores them in memory. The waveform that appears on the screen is a reconstruction from the memory contents put in order.

The scope display represents values of voltage or current on a vertical scale, and values of time on a horizontal scale. The lower left hand corner represents zero values or negative values, depending on the configuration. The values of the vertical divisions are selectable using hand switches or software, and are sometimes expressed as the value of the entire scale, such as a total value of 25 volts from the zero line up to the top of the scale. Other choices might include .1, .5, 1.0, 5, 10, 15 volts, etc.

Much like setting up a multimeter, begin with a value higher than expected, and work your way lower until the waveform occupies an area of the screen that lets you see the desired portion. The horizontal line values of time are also selectable manually, and can range from a few milliseconds up to many whole seconds. The easiest scopes to use have preprogrammed settings made available by the manufacturer, and those settings are set automatically by the software according to the type of circuit or component to be tested, such as fuel injectors, hall effect pickups, and many more.

The preprogrammed settings also control the manner of sweep triggering required for the function selected. Some scopes allow you to program and save your favorite settings and reference waveforms for future recall. You can devise your own trigger points and polarities as you see fit using a manual override. Many units allow you to view multiple traces at the same time, allowing you to compare events in real time, such as comparing an input and output of a module to see if it responds as required.

EXHAUST GAS ANALYSIS

The exhaust gases emitted into the atmosphere are a combination of burned and unburned fuel. To understand the exhaust emission and its composition, we must review some basic chemistry.

When the air/fuel mixture is introduced into the engine, we are mixing air composed of nitrogen (78 percent), oxygen (21 percent) and other gases (1 percent) with the fuel, which is 100 percent HC (Hydrocarbons), in a semi-controlled ratio. As the combustion process is accomplished, power is produced to move the vehicle while the heat of combustion is transferred to the cooling system. The exhaust gases are then composed of N_2 (Nitrogen, a diatomic gas), the same as was introduced in the engine, CO_2 (Carbon Dioxide), the same gas that is

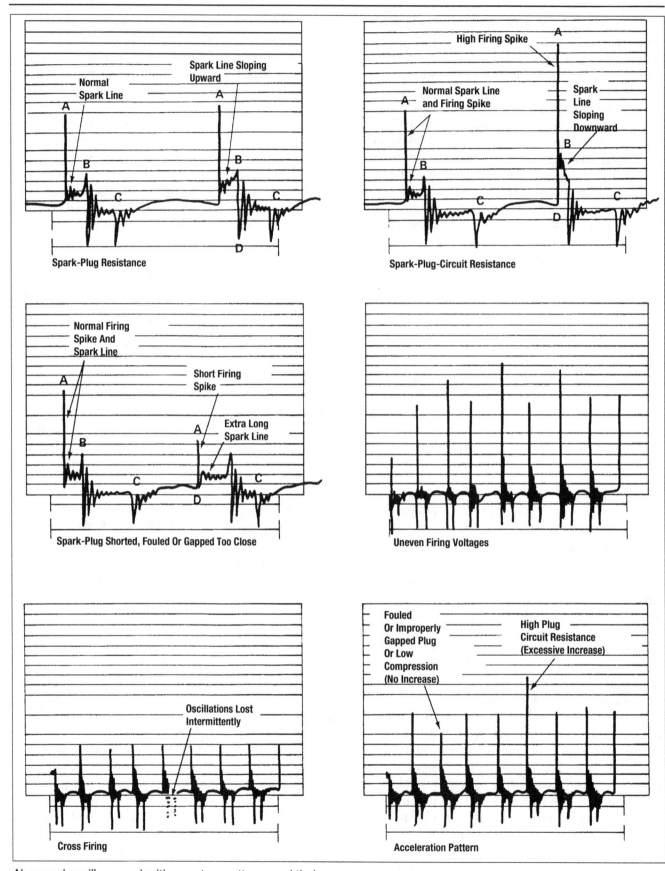

Abnormal oscilloscope ignition system patterns and their causes.

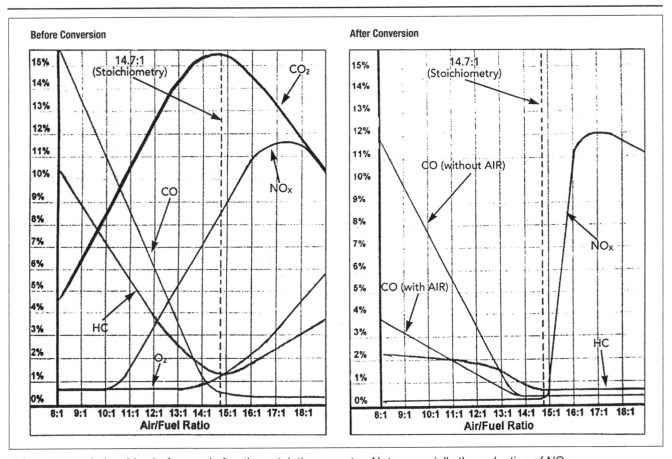

Exhaust gas relationships before and after the catalytic converter. Note especially the reduction of NOx.

used in beverage carbonation, and H_2O (water vapor). The N_2, for the most part, passes through the engine unchanged, while the O_2 (Oxygen) reacts (burns) with the HC and produces the CO_2 and the water vapors. If this chemical process would be the only process to take place, the exhaust emissions would be harmless. However, during the combustion process, other compounds are formed which are considered dangerous. These pollutants are HC, CO (Carbon Monoxide), NOx (Oxides of Nitrogen), SOx (Oxides of Sulfur), and engine particulates.

Interpreting Exhaust Gas Readings

Exhaust gas analyzers are commonly used to check tailpipe emissions levels as a part of states' vehicle inspection programs, but they can also be a valuable diagnostic tool. By checking the quality of

an engine's exhaust, combustion problem areas can be identified according to the type and amount of deviation from normal.

Traditional exhaust gas analyzers read two gases: HC and CO. HC is unburned fuel in the exhaust, and it means that complete combustion is not occurring in the combustion chamber. HC is measured in either parts per million or grams per mile. CO is a colorless, odorless, poisonous gas that's a byproduct of combustion. CO is usually caused by a lack of air or excessive fuel and is measured as a percent of the total exhaust.

As a rule, the more efficiently the engine runs, the less HC and CO it produces. Some manufacturers list CO guidelines for their vehicles. Emission analyzer companies also publish troubleshooting guidelines for HC/CO limits.

CO is a fuel mixture indicator.

The higher the CO level, the richer the mixture; the lower the CO, the leaner the mixture. Anything that enriches the mixture will raise the CO level. Therefore, CO is particularly helpful for diagnosing fuel economy complaints. Everything from leaking injectors to a dirty air filter will raise CO levels. Air leaks, on the other hand, will lower CO levels. Excessive CO emissions could be caused by one or more of the following:

- air/fuel ratio too rich
- clogged air filter
- • leaking fuel injector(s) or fuel pressure regulator diaphragm
- fuel pressure that is too high
- crankcase oil is contaminated with fuel
- engine is running too cool
- faulty sensors, particularly ECT (Engine Coolant Temperature) or IAT (Intake Air Temperature) sensors.

Higher-than-normal HC means engine efficiency is suffering somewhat. Very high HC levels mean the engine is misfiring. When you see high HC, check the CO level: very high HC coupled with very low CO means lean misfire. With these readings, the engine is also likely to have symptoms of rough idle, stalling, hesitation and poor fuel economy; a lower-than-normal manifold vacuum at idle; uneven rpm drops on the power balance test; and a tendency to idle faster and more smoothly when you artificially enrich the mixture.

But, if CO levels are normal, the high HC is caused by ignition or compression-related misfiring.

Excessive HC emissions could be caused by one or more of the following:

- ignition misfires
- incorrect ignition timing
- • air/fuel ratio is too lean or too rich
- low compression
- bad head gasket
- internal engine mechanical problems: bad valves, valve guides, lifters, pistons, piston rings, etc.

The addition of catalytic converters as a part of most vehicle's emissions control systems has greatly reduced the amount of HC and CO in the exhaust, to the point where checking the content of these gases in the exhaust does not give a true indication of engine operation. Four gas analyzers, which monitor CO_2 and O_2 in addition to HC and CO, are now used to measure engine efficiency, since CO_2 and O_2 are changed only slightly by emissions controls. Some exhaust gas analyzers can now also measure NOx.

A high level of CO_2 in the exhaust indicates complete combustion. Any deviation, rich or lean, from the optimum air/fuel ratio will cause the CO_2 level to drop.

To determine whether a low CO_2 level is caused by a rich or lean condition, look at the O_2 levels. Higher O_2 levels indicate a lean mixture, while lower levels mean a richer mixture.

Normally, nitrogen is an inert gas, however, when it is heated to approximately 2500°F (1371°C) through the combustion process, it can bond with O_2 molecules and form NOx. High levels of NOx in the exhaust can be caused by lean air/fuel mixtures, a malfunctioning EGR system and cooling system problems.

Before an exhaust gas analyzer can be used it must first go through a warmup and calibration period. If exhaust flow through the analyzer is restricted because of a clogged filter or probe, a warning light will illuminate. The analyzer or vehicle manufacturer may specify that the secondary air injection system be disconnected before performing exhaust gas analysis. Always refer to the vehicle service manual and/or equipment operator's manual for the proper procedure.

VALVES AND VALVE TIMING

There are literally dozens of valve system configurations, and almost as many adjustment specifications and methods of service. Your concern as the technician is to detect an abnormal condition through basic testing on the analyzer, and to recommend additional diagnosis and repair when warranted by the individual situation. This is done most often by observing the cranking amps per cylinder values, and the relative compression figures for each cylinder. These readings will lead you to focus on the individual cylinders, and their associated valves, for additional testing by means of the compression and leakdown tests.

Valve Timing

An engine that lacks power, has low manifold vacuum and consistently low compression readings on all cylinders indicates that valve timing has jumped. If the timing belt or chain jumps enough teeth or breaks, the engine will not start.

To check valve timing on an engine with distributor ignition, remove the distributor cap. On engines with distributorless ignition, remove a valve cover or timing belt/chain cover. Rotate the crankshaft by hand while watching for distributor rotor or camshaft movement. If the rotor or camshaft does not move when the crankshaft is turned, the belt or chain is broken.

If this is the case, check service information to see whether the engine is a freewheeling or interference engine. On freewheeling engines, the pistons cannot contact the valves regardless of their positions. However, a broken timing belt or timing chain, or one that has excessively jumped time, can result in valve to piston contact on interference engines.

If the rotor or cam moved when the crank was turned, move the crank back and forth to see how much the crank moves before the rotor or cam moves. If there is excessive movement, suspect a loose chain or belt or worn gears.

Accessing and checking the timing mark alignment on the cam and crank sprockets is the best way to see if the engine has jumped time, but another way to determine this is by looking at the valves when the piston is at TDC on the exhaust stroke. At this crankshaft position, both valves should be open slightly because of valve overlap. The exhaust valve should be just closing and the intake valve should be just opening. When the crank is moved slightly back and forth, both valves should move. If the valves do not operate as described with the crank in this position, the valve timing is incorrect.

Valve Adjustment

Assuring proper valve opening and closing on individual cylinders is accomplished by checking the valve adjustment. Engines with mechanical lifters have a valve lash (clearance) setting that must be set within the range specified by the manufacturer. This compensates for thermal expansion. If the clearance is too tight, the valves will be held open causing compression loss and/or valve burning. If the clearance is too loose, the valvetrain will be noisy and the cam will experience shock loads and premature wear. Engine performance can also be adversely affected by the decreased valve lift and changed duration that results.

To adjust valve lash for one cylinder's cam lobes, rotate the crankshaft so that its piston is at TDC on its compression stroke. This will position the intake and exhaust valve lifters or OHC cam followers on the base circle of their respective cam lobes. With the engine in this position, adjust the clearance with a feeler gauge of the proper thickness.

Adjusting valve lash on pushrod engines calls for inserting a feeler gauge between the tip of the valve stem and the rocker arm. An adjustment nut or screw is turned to change the clearance. Occasionally there is a lock nut.

Some OHC engines use lash pad adjusters. These are shims housed in buckets that ride directly on the camshaft. They are replaced to change valve clearance. Other OHC engines use rocker arms that have an adjustment feature on one of their outer ends.

Pay attention to whether the valve lash setting recommended by the manufacturer is a hot or cold

specification. With a cold specification, the lash setting requires no further adjustment once the engine is warm. A hot setting will have to be readjusted once the engine is at normal operating temperature.

On engines with hydraulic lifters, the purpose of valve adjustment is to properly position the hydraulic lifter plunger within the lifter body. This is done by turning the rocker arm adjuster nut a specified amount after zero lash. Most engines with hydraulic lifters have non-adjustable valvetrains; the hydraulic lifter plunger adjustment is designed into the valvetrain geometry. Keep in mind that on these engines, changes in valve stem height resulting from valve and seat grinding or excessive cylinder head or block deck resurfacing can cause a pushrod to move the plunger lower in the lifter body and possibly bottom out in its bore. Different length pushrods can be used to restore the plunger-to-lifter body relationship.

COOLING SYSTEM

Proper engine operation depends on the cooling system maintaining engine operating temperature within a specified range. If the engine runs colder than normal, a richer air/fuel mixture may result, causing poor fuel mileage and excessive emissions. If the engine runs hotter than normal, it may cause detonation or the engine may overheat, resulting in possible engine damage.

Cooling System Inspection

Begin cooling system inspection by checking the coolant appearance, level and freeze protection. The coolant should appear clean and translucent; a cloudy or muddy appearance is evidence of contamination. Check the coolant level in the expansion or overflow tank. The coolant should be at the

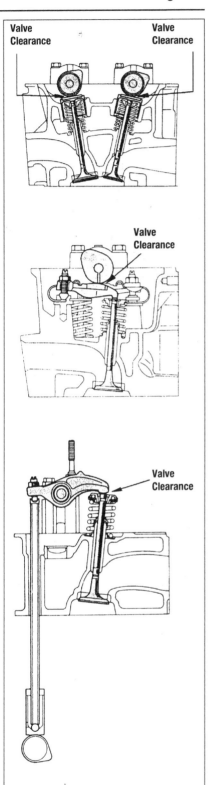

Use a feeler gauge to measure valve clearance (lash). The clearance measuring locations for different valvetrain designs are shown here *(Courtesy: Toyota Motor Sales, USA, Inc.)*

When adjusting a hydraulic lifter, turn the pushrod while tightening the rocker arm adjusting nut to feel for zero lash, then turn the adjusting nut additionally to position the plunger in the lifter body

level indicated for the temperature of the coolant.

Check coolant concentration using a hydrometer. A hydrometer uses a calibrated float to measure the specific gravity of a liquid. The specific gravity of coolant changes according to the antifreeze concentration; the specific gravity increases as the concentration of the antifreeze increases.

It is best to obtain a coolant sample directly from the radiator, as the overflow tank may have recently been topped off with water or pure antifreeze. Always use caution when removing the radiator cap from a pressurized system; only remove the cap when the system is cold. Draw the coolant into the hydrometer and read the specific gravity on the float. The protection level should be at least –34°F (–37°C), which represents a 50/50 mixture of antifreeze and water.

Visually inspect the cooling system for problems. Check for signs of coolant leaks at all hose connections, core plugs (freeze plugs), head gasket(s), thermostat housing, water pump and radiator. Inspect all hoses for cracks, ballooning or brittleness and replace if necessary. If the hoses feel soft or mushy

when they are squeezed, replace them.

Check the radiator for restrictions in the air passages through the core. Clean the fins of debris, bugs or leaves that may have been drawn in while driving. Sometimes, debris may collect between the radiator and condenser. Make sure all fins are intact, and not bent so as to misdirect air flow. Distorted fins can be straightened using a suitable tool, however, be careful when straightening because the fins are very delicate.

Inspect the radiator for damage and any signs of leakage from the core tubes, radiator tanks and hose collars. Look inside the radiator for large amounts of mineral deposits at the ends of the core tubes, as mineral buildup can cause an internal restriction. If blockage inside the radiator is suspected, an infrared surface thermometer can be used to scan the surface of the radiator when the engine is hot and idling. The radiator should be warmest near the inlet and gradually cool toward the outlet. If there are areas that are considerably cooler than the inlet, then there may be restrictions at those areas.

Check the radiator cap rating to

make sure it is the right one for the vehicle. Check the cap's relief valve spring action, and inspect the seal for brittleness. Check the filler neck on the radiator or surge tank mating surface.

Check the water pump drive belt for wear, glazing and belt tension. A slipping belt will not turn the pump impeller at the proper speed to circulate coolant. If the engine is equipped with a mechanical fan, a slipping belt will cause the fan to turn too slowly, not draw enough air through the radiator, and possibly cause the engine to overheat. Replace or adjust the belt as necessary.

Check for a coolant leak from the vent hole at the bottom of the water pump shaft housing. Check the water pump bearings by grasping the fan or pulley and attempt to move the impeller shaft back and forth. If there is any movement, the water pump bearings are defective. Remove the drive belt and turn the pulley by hand. The pulley should turn smoothly. If there is noise and/or binding, the bearings are defective. Replace the pump if it leaks or the bearings are defective.

Inspect the fan for missing, cracked or bent blades. If equipped with a fan clutch, check the back of the clutch for an oily film, which would indicate that fluid is leaking and replacement is necessary. Turn the fan and clutch assembly by hand; there should be some viscous drag, but it should turn smoothly during a full rotation. Replace the fan clutch if it does not turn smoothly or if it does not turn at all. It should also be replaced if there is no viscous drag when hot or cold.

If the fan is electric, make sure it runs when the engine warms up and also when the A/C is switched on. Make sure the fan shroud is in place and not broken.

Start the engine and listen for unusual noises. A hammering sound may indicate a restriction in the water jacket or air in the system. Squealing noises indicate a bad belt or water pump bearing damage. Gurgling from the radiator may point to air in the system.

The engine's operating temperature can be verified by installing a mechanical gauge or by using a hand held pyrometer.

Cooling System Pressure Testing

Use a hand-held pump with a pressure gauge that is designed for cooling system testing. While the engine is cold, remove the pressure cap from the radiator or surge tank. Make sure the system is filled to capacity, then attach the tester. Pump it up to the rated system pressure and watch the gauge needle; it should not drop rapidly. If pressure drops, check for leaks at the radiator and heater hoses, water pump, radiator, intake manifold, sensor fittings, water control valves and heater core. Repair leaks as required and retest.

If you can't spot the leak, it may be internal such as a head gasket, cracked cylinder head or cracked block. Inspect the engine oil for signs of coolant; if it is thick and milky, that's a dead giveaway.

If coolant is leaking into a cylinder, combustion gases will also be able to escape into the cooling system. When combustion gas escapes into the cooling system, it can cause big air bubbles to appear in the radiator coolant when the engine is running. It can also pressurize the coolant recovery reservoir. An internal coolant leak can be detected by placing a vial of a chemical that is sensitive to combustion gases over the radiator filler neck while the engine is running. The chemical will change color in the presence of combustion gases. An exhaust analyzer probe can also be held over the filler neck while checking for a reading on the ex-

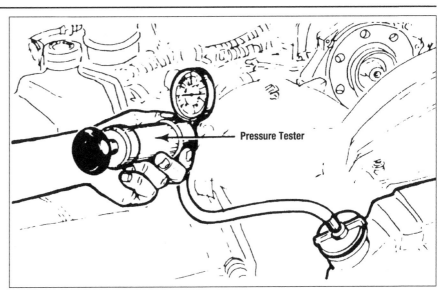

Pressure testing the cooling system. Watch the gauge needle for an indication of a cooling system leak.

haust analyzer.

The coolant may be going out the tailpipe, however, which would be indicated by white smoke from the exhaust pipe and a somewhat sweet antifreeze odor in the exhaust. Remember that catalytic converters can mask small coolant leak symptoms, because the converter superheats the coolant into such a fine vapor that it is not noticeable.

Use the system tester's cap adapter to check the pressure cap. Pump it up to the cap's rating. It should hold for about 10 seconds and then decrease just a bit. If it drops too much, replace the cap. Pump the cap to exceed its pressure rating. The cap should release pressure; if not it should be replaced.

COOLING FANS

Mechanical Cooling Fan

Most rear-wheel-drive cars and trucks have belt-driven, mechanical fans equipped with a fan clutch. The fan clutch is designed to slip when cold and rotate the fan at certain maximum speeds when hot. Fan clutches improve gas mileage and reduce noise levels.

Inspect the fan clutch as described earlier in this section.

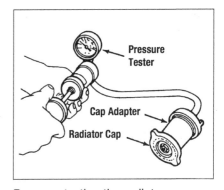

Pressure testing the radiator cap.

To test the fan clutch, attach a thermometer or electronic temperature probe to the radiator near the inlet and connect a timing light to the engine. Start the engine and strobe the fan to 'freeze' the blades; note the engine speed. When the engine warms up (check the thermometer), the fan speed should increase and the blades will appear to be moving in the strobe light. As the temperature drops, the fan should slow down. A quick check of fan clutches is to shut down a hot engine, then observe how long it takes for the fan to stop spinning. A properly operating clutch should stop the fan from spinning within two seconds.

Replace the fan clutch if it fails inspection or testing.

Electric Cooling Fan

Many vehicles, especially those with transverse engines, use electric cooling fans. Besides not needing a belt to drive them, electric fans conserve energy since they run only when needed.

When the engine slightly exceeds proper operating temperature, the electric fan should come on. It may cycle on and off as the coolant warms and cools. On most vehicles, the fan also should run whenever the A/C is switched on. (Some vehicles have two fans with one dedicated to the A/C system. That one may not run for engine cooling alone.)

If the fan doesn't run, visually inspect the wiring and connectors in the circuit and check the fuse. Make sure the operating conditions (coolant temperature, A/C on) exist that would engage the fan. Check the voltage at the fan relay terminals and fan motor using a DMM (Digital Multi-meter), according to the manufacturer's diagnostic procedure.

WIRING DIAGRAMS

The ability to read and understand electrical schematics is a necessity for diagnosing engine performance problems. Since wiring diagrams are like a road map of the electrical system, trying to trace electrical problems without them makes the job twice as hard. Circuits in vehicles contain numerous components, and many different circuits may share some of the same wires.

Wiring diagrams indicate circuit identification factors like wire colors, connector types and locations. This is vital information when diagnosing electrical problems. But, before a technician begins his search, he must be certain that the diagram is in fact the correct one for the vehicle. Revisions and changes to wiring har-

nesses can take place, causing confusion. Also, always look for a legend on the wiring diagram indicating which symbols represent which components. Different manufacturers might use different symbols to represent the same components.

Review the table of symbols shown in this study guide, and make it a point to learn the various ways different manufacturers typically show their circuits in manuals. Symbols are usually self-explanatory, such as the symbol for a bulb clearly showing the curl of the filament and the one for a battery looking like plates sandwiched together.

In every diagram, a line shown between symbols is an electrical pathway between components, usually a wire or cable. Sometimes, an entire group of circuits are summarized in a block or square on the diagram because too many components are contained within. Commonly, power connections are on the top and bottom of a schematic, and input and output circuits are depicted to the left and right, but all of this can vary with the particular schematic.

If simplified schematics aren't available for a given vehicle, don't be intimidated by the more complex type that shows several circuits lumped together. Just make a photocopy of the schematic and highlight the circuit you are inter-

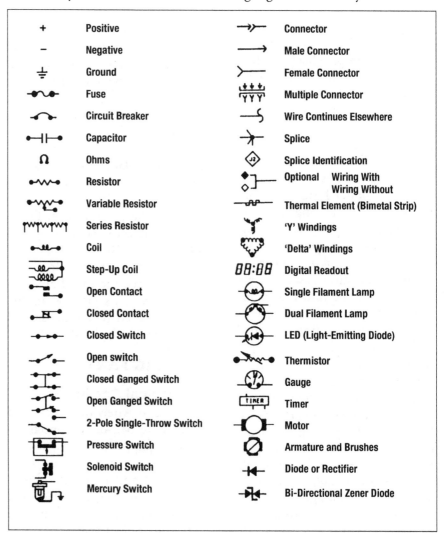

+	Positive			Connector
–	Negative			Male Connector
	Ground			Female Connector
	Fuse			Multiple Connector
	Circuit Breaker			Wire Continues Elsewhere
	Capacitor			Splice
Ω	Ohms			Splice Identification
	Resistor			Optional Wiring With / Wiring Without
	Variable Resistor			Thermal Element (Bimetal Strip)
	Series Resistor			'Y' Windings
	Coil			'Delta' Windings
	Step-Up Coil		88:88	Digital Readout
	Open Contact			Single Filament Lamp
	Closed Contact			Dual Filament Lamp
	Closed Switch			LED (Light-Emitting Diode)
	Open switch			Thermistor
	Closed Ganged Switch			Gauge
	Open Ganged Switch		TIMER	Timer
	2-Pole Single-Throw Switch			Motor
	Pressure Switch			Armature and Brushes
	Solenoid Switch			Diode or Rectifier
	Mercury Switch			Bi-Directional Zener Diode

Typical electrical symbols used in automotive wiring diagrams and schematics.

ested in. It's often helpful to re-draw it on a separate piece of paper in simplified fashion. Straighten out the wires and arrange the components so you can understand the intended current path. This may seem like a lot of trouble, but a clear schematic can shorten your work time substantially.

BATTERY

Preliminary Inspection

WARNING: The sulfuric acid in battery electrolyte can cause serious injury if it contacts the eyes or skin. To prevent injury, always wear skin and eye protection when servicing the battery. Batteries give off hydrogen gas, which is highly explosive. Never smoke or allow flames near a battery.

Visually inspect the battery, looking for damage to the battery case and damage or corrosion on the battery terminals and cables. If the battery case is damaged and there is any evidence of leakage, the battery must be replaced. Check the battery's date of manufacture. Just because the battery is near the end of its service life does not mean that it will necessarily test bad, however the age of the battery must be considered when deciding whether replacement is necessary.

Corrosion on the battery case, and battery tray and hold-down, can be cleaned with a solution of baking soda and water. Make sure the battery tray is in good condition and the battery is mounted securely, without over-tightening the battery hold-down.

If the battery terminals and cables are corroded, remove the cables, negative cable first, and clean the terminals and cables with a battery brush. Before discon-necting the battery cables, keep in mind that computers, programmable radios, and other solid-state memory units may have their memories erased by disconnecting the battery. In addition, the engine and transmission on some vehicles may perform erratically when first started and must undergo a relearning process, once the battery is reconnected. To prevent this, a 12-volt power supply from a dry cell battery can be connected to the cigarette lighter or power point connector to maintain voltage in the system while the battery is disconnected.

Inspect the entire length of the battery cables for heavy corrosion, frayed wires and damaged insulation, and replace as necessary. Secure the cables to the battery terminals after cleaning, and apply a coating of petroleum jelly to the terminals to minimize further corrosion.

If the battery has removable vent caps, check the electrolyte condition and level in each battery cell. Look for cloudy or muddy discoloration of the fluid. Discolored fluid is a sign of recent deep cycle discharge action. Add distilled water to the proper level, if necessary. In general, the electrolyte should be 1/4 - 1/2-in. (6.35 - 12.70mm) above the plates.

Battery State-of-Charge

A hydrometer can be used to check the specific gravity of the battery's electrolyte if the vent caps are removable. The glass tube of the hydrometer is scale-calibrated to read specific gravity in a range of about 1.100 to 1.300.

The floats in the hydrometer are calibrated with 80°F (27°C) being the exact reference point. For each 10°F variation above or below the 80°F (27°C) mark, 0.004 specific gravity points are added (for temperatures above 80°F) or subtracted (for tem-peratures below 80°F).

A battery with a specific gravity reading of 1.260 (usually stated as twelve-sixty) is generally regarded as fully charged, while a battery with a reading of 1.070 (ten-seventy) is generally regarded as fully discharged. It follows that 1.120 is one-quarter charged; 1.170 is half-charged; and 1.215 is three-quarters charged. A maximum of 0.050 (50 points) difference between cells is all that is allowed. Any difference greater than this calls for further testing of the battery, and the battery may have to be removed from service.

When checking specific gravity, hold the hydrometer in a vertical position and insert the draw tube into the battery. Draw just enough electrolyte into the tube to permit the float to move freely without touching the top, bottom, or sides. Note that there are times when electrolyte readings are inaccurate. One is just after adding water to the battery. After adding water, it is recommended to wait at least one day, or until the vehicle has been operated for a while to check specific gravity. Another time is during or just after charging. After charging, it is recommended to wait at

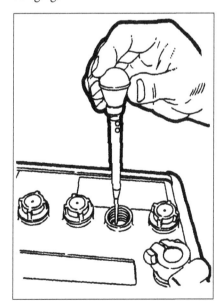

Checking electrolyte specific gravity with a hydrometer.

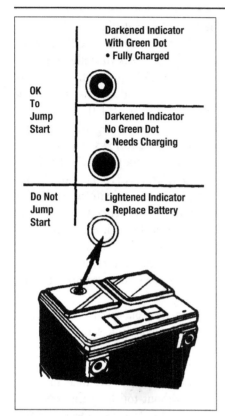

Charge indicator on a sealed maintenance-free battery.

least 15 minutes prior to checking specific gravity. Still another time is just after the battery has been subjected to a high rate of discharge, such as after prolonged cranking.

The electrolyte cannot be checked on sealed maintenance-free batteries. However, some of these batteries have a built-in hydrometer. Although the readings can vary according to manufacturer, usually a good battery is indicated by a green or light-colored dot in the center. If the indicator is dark, the battery may be jumped or recharged. If the indicator is clear or light yellow, the fluid level is below the level of the hydrometer; the battery should not be charged and should be replaced. Always refer to the label on the battery or the battery manufacturer's instructions to interpret battery condition using the built-in hydrometer. Also, be aware that the built-in hydrometer indicates the condition of only one cell.

Check the open circuit voltage of

the battery to determine if it must be charged before further testing. Remove the surface charge from the battery by turning on the high beams for 10 seconds, then wait a few seconds before checking the battery voltage. Make sure all accessories are off, then measure the voltage at the battery terminals with a voltmeter. If the voltage is less than 12.4 volts, the battery must be charged before proceeding with further testing.

Battery Capacity Testing

Connect the battery load tester to the battery terminals. Turn the load control knob to draw current equal to three times the ampere-hour (amp/hr) rating or one-half the CCA (Cold Cranking Amps) rating. The battery rating is usually given on the battery case, case top or label, and some labels will indicate the load that should be placed on the battery. Maintain the load for 15 seconds, then check the voltage reading. On a good battery, the voltage should be 9.6 volts or higher, however the voltage may be slightly lower if the ambient temperature is less than 70°F (21°C).

If a battery fails a load test, but was deemed OK for testing when the state-of-charge was checked, connect a voltmeter and battery charger to the battery and charge the battery for three minutes with the charger set at 40 amps. If after three minutes the voltage reading is greater than 15.5 volts, replace the battery.

Key Off Battery Drain

Excessive circuit drain when the vehicle is not running can lead to battery depletion, even if the battery is in good condition and the charging system is in proper working order.

The main reason for a very slight draw on the battery is the fact that major computerized systems in the vehicle need voltage at all times in order to function properly. Components such as computer memories and stored

diagnostic data must be kept whether the vehicle is running or not. The digital clock and other such items also draw a very small current while the vehicle is off. This is not a problem for today's vehicles as long as the drain is not excessive.

Sometimes, it's hard to tell whether there is a key off battery drain because the drain won't be enough to completely discharge the battery while the vehicle is off. The only way this type of drain manifests itself is by excessive battery water usage and the fact that the battery doesn't last as long as it should with a known good charging and starting system. Always use the manufacturer's suggested key off drain specifications when trying to determine the proper amount of current that computer systems and accessories should draw when the vehicle's engine is not running.

Using a 12-volt test light in series with a battery cable is not the most accurate way to check for key off battery drain. The most effective way of checking this condition is to use an ammeter in series with the negative battery cable and the negative battery post. This enables full battery voltage to the vehicle during the measurement. Another method that can be used is to measure voltage drop across a 1-ohm resistor connected in series between the negative battery cable and the negative battery post, using a DMM.

NOTE: Make sure the ignition switch is in the OFF position at all times during testing. In addition, all courtesy and accessory lights must be off.

If an excessive drain is displayed, remove the fuses from the fuse block one at a time. When the specific fuse powering the circuit with the drain is removed, the high voltage reading will stabilize to a normal reading.

Using a wiring diagram, note the

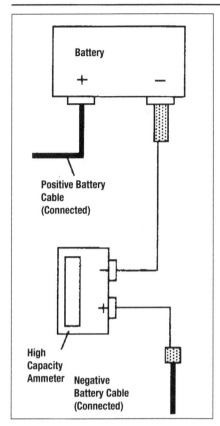

Battery electrical drain check.
(Courtesy: GM Corp.)

specific circuits that run to the particular fuse that was pulled. Reinstall the fuse and allow the DMM to read the excessive draw. Now, disconnect each circuit to further isolate the current draw. When the draw returns to normal, you've found the circuit that's causing the problem.

If the drain is not found using this procedure, use a wiring diagram and locate all circuits connected to the battery that use a fusible link. Disconnect the circuits, one at a time, to isolate the circuit with the excessive draw. A fusible link is a fused wire that protects a particular circuit from high currents, and may be either in a harness, or mounted separately, and performs the same function as the fuse in a fuse block.

STARTING SYSTEM

Starter Current Draw Test

Perform a starter current-draw

test with a high-amperage-rated ammeter designed for this purpose. Allow the engine to warm up to normal operating temperature, then disable the ignition system on gasoline engines or fuel system on diesel engines. Connect the ammeter's inductive pickup to the negative battery cable or connect the ammeter in series with the negative battery cable. Also, connect a voltmeter across the battery terminals.

With the test connections made and all electrical loads off, crank the engine over with the starter. Starter current draw when cranking the engine over should be around 150 amps for a 4-cylinder engine, 200 amps for a 6-cylinder and 250 amps for a V8, however, some permanent magnet type and gear reduction starters can draw more. Always refer to the specifications in the vehicle service manual. Battery voltage should remain above 9.6V, and the engine should spin rapidly.

Higher than normal current-draw readings may be caused by a short circuit in the starter motor or mechanical problems causing binding in the engine. Amperage that is too low may be caused by starter circuit resistance.

Voltage Drop Test

Connect the voltmeter black lead to the battery cable connection at the starter. Make sure the test point is positioned after the starter

relay. Now, disable the engine ignition and crank the starter motor. As you crank the engine, touch the red lead of the voltmeter to the positive post of the battery. Quickly switch the voltage scale knob of the voltmeter to progressively lower scales until a reading

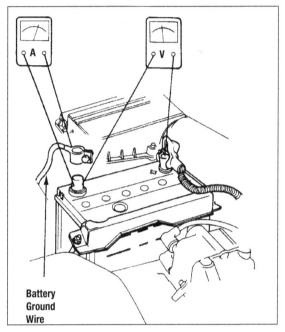

Performing a starter current draw test.
(Courtesy: Honda Motor Co.)

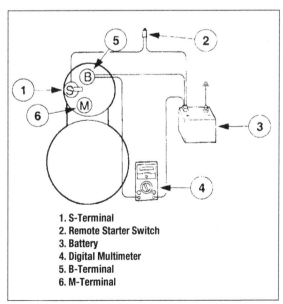

1. S-Terminal
2. Remote Starter Switch
3. Battery
4. Digital Multimeter
5. B-Terminal
6. M-Terminal

Performing a starter voltage drop test.
(Courtesy: Ford Motor Co.)

can be seen. Be sure to remove the red voltmeter lead from the battery post before you release the starter engagement, or you could damage the meter.

If the voltage drop exceeds 0.5V for the entire starter circuit, repeat the test, moving the black lead toward the battery one connection at a time. When you get past the bad one, the voltage drop reading will sharply decline. Once the high resistance connection is identified, clean the connection or replace the part causing the problem. Refer to the proper service manual for the manufacturer's maximum acceptable voltage drop specifications.

Starter Ground And Connection

To check the starter ground circuit, first place the black lead of the voltmeter on the negative battery post. Now, using the same technique you used on the supply voltage circuit, crank the starter and place the red lead on the starter housing. Read the voltage drop. If you find a high resistance at the starter mounting, the presence of engine-to-starter shims, or an engine-to-battery ground cable that produces more than the voltage drop recommended by the manufacturer, check carefully for a poor connection or even corrosion.

Locate the problem by moving the red lead closer to the battery post in steps. Repeat the voltage test each time. Don't forget to remove the red lead before you stop cranking the engine!

Now check the control circuit. Locate the starter relay or solenoid and place the black voltmeter lead on the relay control voltage terminal. Crank the engine over and place the red lead to the positive battery terminal to check the voltage drop. This checks the circuit through the ignition switch, neutral

safety switch and wiring harness.

Remember to check the relay ground. Quite often, relays are mounted on non-metallic inner fender panels and require a good ground to the metal car body.

Starter Relay

Some starting systems use a relay between the ignition switch and starter solenoid. When the ignition key is turned to start, current flows to the relay, closing the relay contacts. When the relay contacts close, current from the battery flows to the starter solenoid.

To test the relay, measure the voltage at the relay switch terminal and starter terminal and compare to specifications. If the voltage is less than specified at the switch terminal, there is a problem in the

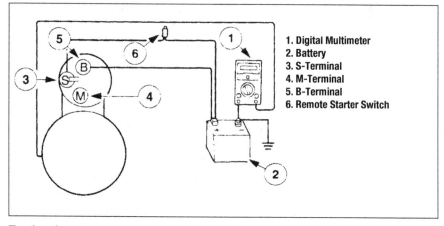

Testing the starter ground circuit.   (Courtesy: Ford Motor Co.)

1. Digital Multimeter
2. Battery
3. S-Terminal
4. M-Terminal
5. B-Terminal
6. Remote Starter Switch

control circuit upstream of the relay. If the voltage is as specified at the switch terminal but not at the starter terminal, the relay should be replaced.

The starter relay can be mounted in the engine compartment on the firewall or inner fender, or plug into an underhood fuse and relay box. To replace the former type, disconnect the negative battery cable and mark and remove the wires from the relay. Loosen the fasteners and remove the relay from its mounting. Before install-

ing a replacement relay, check all cables and connections for corrosion and proper routing. Clean and make repairs as necessary. To install the relay, reverse the removal procedure.

Starter Solenoid

A starter solenoid is an electromagnetic switch. It may be remotely mounted away from the starter, on the firewall or inner fender, or it may be mounted on the starter motor. Remote mounted solenoids open or close the battery-to-starter circuit. Starter mounted solenoids do this as well, but also push the starter drive gear into mesh with the flywheel/ flexplate ring gear.

When voltage is provided to a starter mounted solenoid from the ignition switch or starter relay, the starter solenoid is energized, creating a magnetic field in the solenoid coil and drawing in an iron plunger core into the coil. A lever connected to the starter drive engages the drive gear with the flywheel/flexplate ring gear. When the iron plunger core is all the way into the coil, its contact disc closes the circuit between the battery and the starter motor terminals. Current flows to the motor and the drive gear turns the flywheel/flexplate.

As current flows to the motor, the solenoid pull-in coil is bypassed and the hold-in coil keeps the drive gear engaged with the flywheel/flexplate. The gear remains engaged until the ignition switch is released from the start position.

The starter solenoid can be tested in the same manner as the starter relay. The solenoid can also be tested using a jumper wire between the battery and solenoid 'S' terminals. If the engine cranks, there is a problem in the starter control circuit. If the solenoid makes a clicking sound, it is operating properly and the problem may be with the starter. If no sound is heard, the solenoid is defective and should be replaced.

To replace a remote solenoid, disconnect the negative battery cable and mark and remove the wires from the solenoid. Loosen the fasteners and remove the solenoid from its mounting. Before installing a replacement solenoid, check

all cables and connections for corrosion and proper routing. Clean and make repairs as necessary. To install the solenoid, reverse the removal procedure.

To replace a starter mounted solenoid, disconnect the negative battery cable, then mark and remove the wires from the solenoid. If necessary, remove the starter from the vehicle. Remove the mounting bolts for the solenoid. You may have to rotate the solenoid to remove it from the starter, as some solenoids have a tab that fits in the starter housing. In addition, the plunger spring puts a slight tension on the solenoid.

When installing the solenoid, make sure the spring is in place between the plunger and the solenoid body. Hold the solenoid and compress the spring. If necessary, locate the tab and rotate the solenoid into position. Install the solenoid mounting bolts. If removed, install the starter motor. Reconnect

the starter wires and the negative battery cable and check for proper operation.

Neutral Start Switch

The neutral start switch prevents vehicles with automatic transmissions from starting in gear positions other than Neutral or Park. The switch can be located on the steering column, shift lever or transmission.

To check the switch, apply the brakes and move the gearshift lever through each position while holding the ignition key in the Start position. If the starter operates in gear positions other than Neutral or Park, the switch may only need adjustment.

To adjust the switch, place the transmission in Park and loosen the switch mounting screws. Turn the ignition key to the start position and move the switch until the starter operates. Hold the switch in that position, release the igni-

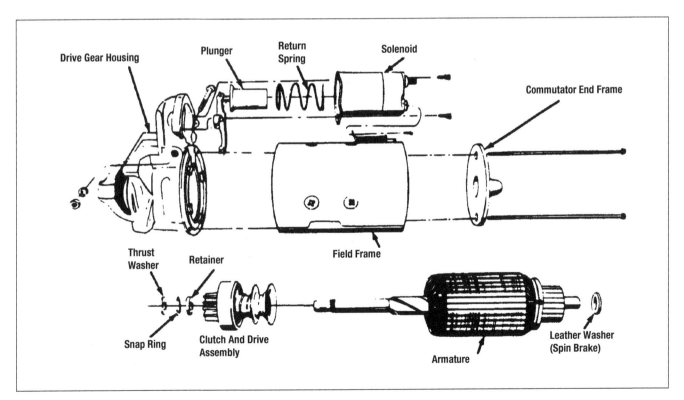

Exploded view of a typical starter and starter-mounted solenoid.
(Courtesy: GM Corp.)

tion key and tighten the switch mounting screws. Check switch operation.

To electrically test the switch, touch a 12-volt test light to the switch output wire while moving the gearshift lever through each position. The test light should be on only when the gearshift is in Neutral or Park. If the light works otherwise, check the device that actuates the switch. If that is OK, replace the switch.

Clutch Switch

The start/clutch interlock switch is a safety device that prevents the engine from starting with the transmission in gear. It prevents the starter from operating unless the clutch pedal is depressed.

The switch is open when the clutch pedal is in the released position, interrupting current flow in the starter circuit. When the clutch pedal is depressed, the switch closes, allowing current flow in the circuit. If the starter engages with the clutch pedal released or if it does not engage with the pedal depressed, first check the switch adjustment. Refer to the service manual for specifications.

If adjustment is correct, check for voltage to the input side of the switch. If voltage is present at the input side, there should be no voltage at the output side of the switch when it is in the open position (pedal released), but there should be voltage at the output side when the switch is closed (pedal depressed). Replace the switch if it does not perform as specified.

CHARGING SYSTEM

A charging system can malfunction in several ways: there can be no charging, low charging or overcharging conditions. A no-charging or low charging condition can be caused by a broken or slipping alternator drive belt, defective volt-

age regulator, defective diodes or stator windings, an open alternator field circuit, excessive resistance or an open in the wiring between the alternator and battery, and sulfated battery plates.

Overcharging can be caused by a defective voltage regulator, a shorted field wire and a battery that is internally shorted.

A system that is not charging or undercharging is usually indicated by a discharged battery that does not have enough power to operate the starter or causes the starter to crank slowly, dim headlights, a dash warning light that illuminates or flickers or an ammeter that indicates low charging. Overcharging is indicated by short light bulb life and a battery that continually needs water.

Undercharging can cause the battery plates to sulfate and can cause a high water content in the electrolyte, allowing the battery to freeze in cold weather. Overcharging can cause severe corrosion and warpage to the battery positive plates, excessive heat in the battery that can also damage plates, and electrolyte depletion, which can also cause premature deterioration of the active material in the battery plates.

Preliminary Inspection

Perform a visual inspection to check for obvious problems. Check the alternator drive belt for evidence of cracking, fraying, glazing or other damage and replace as necessary.

If the belt is adjustable, belt tension can be checked using the deflection method or by using a belt tension gauge. Locate a point midway between the pulleys on the longest accessible belt span. If using the deflection method, push on the belt with your finger using moderate pressure and measure the belt deflection. If you are using

a belt tension gauge, position the gauge and measure the amount of force necessary to deflect the belt. Compare your reading with specification.

Belt tension should also be checked on vehicles with automatic belt tensioners to make sure the tensioner is functioning properly. Some automatic tensioners are equipped with belt length indicator and minimum and maximum acceptable marks, the theory being that if the correct length belt is installed on the engine and the mark is within range, belt tension is correct.

To adjust V-belt tension, loosen the adjuster pulley, or alternator pivot and adjuster bolts, then use a suitable prybar to move the pulley or alternator until the belt tension is correct. Tighten all fasteners and recheck belt tension. Make sure the alternator is mounted securely in its mounting brackets.

Inspect and test the battery according to the procedures outlined in the battery service section of this study guide. Check the condition of the battery cables and system wiring, making sure all connections are clean and tight.

General Testing

Use an inductive probe to check the alternator output at the alternator output wire while the charging system analyzer places a calibrated load on the charging system. If no analyzer is available, place the voltmeter on the proper scale for battery voltage and connect the red lead to the positive cable. Connect the black lead to the negative cable.

Start the engine. The base voltage reading should increase by approximately 2 volts if the charging system is working properly, but be sure to consult the appropriate service specification.

Now, place a load on the alterna-

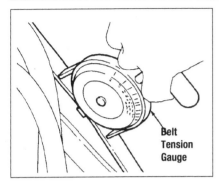

Checking alternator belt tension with a belt tension gauge.
(Courtesy: Ford Motor Co.)

tor by turning on the headlights, or substitute a carbon pile load connected across the battery terminals. Increase the engine speed to about 2000-2500 rpm. The voltage should now read between 13.8V and 14.5V. Switch your meter to the AC scale and be certain that your AC ripple current is not excessive, indicating a failed rectifier diode(s). Use available specifications for the vehicle you are testing.

Isolation Testing

If the amp reading is low, testing must be performed to isolate the problem. Alternator output is controlled by the strength of the field current. By replacing the regulator with manual control of the field, diagnosis of the alternator and regulator circuits can be accomplished.

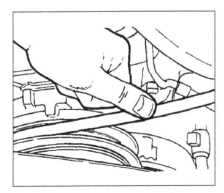

Checking alternator belt tension using the deflection method.

How you substitute and full-field voltage-check the alternator depends on the type of field circuits in the unit. If the alternator is an A-type, the field is grounded AFTER the field (externally grounded). Key on, engine off, you will have a voltage indication on both of the field terminals. If it's a B-unit, the field is controlled BEFORE the field, (internally grounded) by controlling current on the positive side, while the ground on the other side of the field is constant. Check a service manual to determine the exact type of alternator installed in the vehicle on which you are working.

To test an externally-grounded unit (After), make sure all lights

and accessories are off. Set the engine rpm to 1500-2000 rpm. Now ground the field according to the manufacturer's recommended procedure. Full amperage output should be indicated if the alternator is in good condition and being driven properly. Listen for noises while the alternator is under full load.

Test an internally-grounded unit (Before) by supplying full-field voltage to the field terminal of the alternator. Use a full fielding device or a jumper wire to send battery voltage to the field winding for a moment, and watch for a rise in system voltage.

If the alternator produces rated amperage, the regulator circuit is

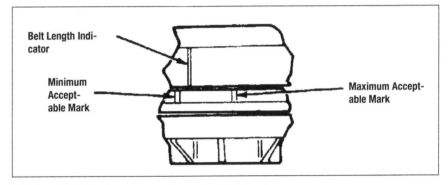

Belt length indicator on an automatic belt tensioner.
(Courtesy: Ford Motor Co.)

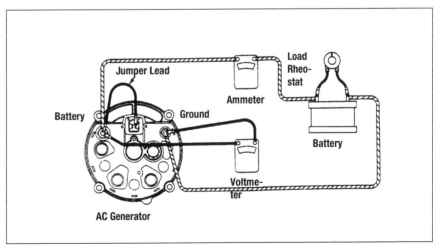

To test maximum charging system output, connect a load rheostat to the battery. Then, connect a jumper wire to the 'FIELD' terminal and the battery terminal to provide a full field. Connect a voltmeter and ammeter to measure total output.

out of adjustment or defective. Perform voltage and continuity checks at the regulator harness plug. Make sure the regulator has an adequate voltage supply from the vehicle harness and that the wires connecting the regulator and the alternator are in good condition.

Charging Circuit Voltage Drop

Excessive resistance in the voltage and/or ground sides of the charging circuit can cause a low charging rate due to the difference between alternator output and electrical system voltage requirements. Charging system voltage drop is usually caused by a defective, incorrect or corroded cable from the alternator to the battery, or a poor ground connection on the negative side of the circuit.

To check for high resistance in the voltage side of the system, connect the voltmeter negative lead to the positive battery cable end. Next, connect the positive lead to the opposing cable end at the alternator. Read the voltage drop and compare with manufacturer's specifications. Normally, the voltage drop should not exceed 0.2 volts.

To check for high resistance in the ground side of the system, connect the voltmeter negative lead to the negative battery cable end. Next, connect the positive lead to the alternator grounding point (usually the alternator bracket). Read the voltage drop and compare with manufacturer's specifications. Normally, the voltage drop should not exceed 0.1 volt.

Drive Belts, Pulleys And Tensioners

Squealing noises from the engine compartment that increase in frequency as the engine rpm is raised, can usually be attributed to a loose belt. In addition, pulley misalignment can cause the belt to enter the alternator pulley on an angle, also causing noise.

Check the alternator belt for wear and proper adjustment as described under preliminary inspection. If replacement is necessary, loosen the adjuster pulley or alternator pivot and adjuster bolts, moving the pulley or alternator to eliminate belt tension, and remove the belt. It may be necessary to remove other accessory drive belts to gain access to the alternator belt.

Before removing a serpentine V-ribbed belt, make sure there is a belt routing diagram handy or draw one prior to belt removal, to prevent installation problems. Use a socket or wrench to tilt the automatic tensioner away from the belt, and then remove the belt from the pulleys.

After the belt is removed, spin the pulley to determine if it wobbles or has any noticeable bearing wear. Inspect the pulleys for chips, nicks, cracks, tool marks, bent sidewalls, severe corrosion or other damage. Check for hard objects such as small stones or sand that may have become imbedded in the bottom of the pulley grooves.

When replacing the belt, inspect the alternator and its corresponding pulley(s) for improper alignment. Aligned pulleys reduce both pulley and belt wear, and vibration of engine components. If the belt pulleys are severely misaligned, look for improper positioning of the alternator or its corresponding pulley, improper fit of the pulley or shaft, or incorrect components installed.

Install a new belt, making sure it is correctly positioned in its pulley grooves and properly routed. Adjust the belt tension, as required.

WIRING REPAIRS

Soldering is a quick, efficient method of joining metals permanently. Everyone who has to make wiring repairs should know how to solder. Electrical connections that are soldered are far less likely to come apart and will conduct electricity much better than connections that are only crimped together.

The most popular — though not the only — method of soldering is with an electrical soldering gun. Soldering irons are available in many sizes and wattage ratings. Irons with higher wattage ratings deliver higher temperatures and recover lost heat faster. A small soldering iron rated for no more than 50 watts is recommended, especially on electrical systems where excess heat can damage the components being soldered. Replacement of alternator pigtails requires a gun that is intended for heavy use, due to the high heat loss through the large diameter wires.

Three ingredients are necessary for successful soldering:
- proper flux
- good solder
- sufficient heat.

A soldering flux is necessary to

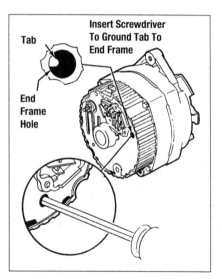

This alternator may be tested for full field strength by grounding a tab showing through the rear window of the housing. Many other vehicles, however, require jumping techniques. The hook-up varies, so always consult the service manual for proper service procedures.

clean the metal of tarnish, prepare it for soldering and enable the solder to spread into tiny crevices. When soldering, always use a rosin flux or rosin core solder that is non-corrosive and will not attract moisture once the job is finished. Other types of flux (acid core) will leave a residue that will attract moisture and cause wires to corrode.

Tin is a unique metal with a low melting point. In a molten state,

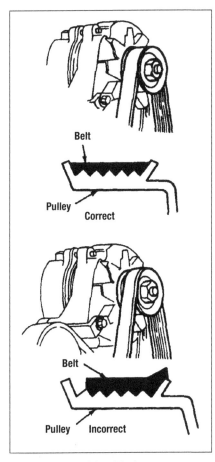

Belt

Pulley **Correct**

Belt

Pulley **Incorrect**

Make sure V-ribbed belts are properly seated in the pulley grooves. One revolution of the engine with the belt incorrectly seated can damage the belt. *(Courtesy: Ford Motor Co.)*

it dissolves and easily forms alloys with many metals. Solder is created by mixing tin with lead. The most common proportions are 40/60, 50/50 and 60/40, with the percentage of tin listed first. Low-priced solders usually contain less tin, making them very difficult for a beginner to use because more heat is required to melt the solder. A common solder is 40/60, which is well suited for general use. But 60/40 melts more easily, has more tin for a better joint, and is preferred for electrical work. It contains the proper flux, and will say 'rosin core' on the package.

Successful soldering requires that the metals to be joined be heated to a temperature that will melt the solder, usually between 360 and 460°F (182-238°C). Contrary to popular belief, the purpose of the soldering iron is not to melt the solder itself, but to heat the parts being soldered to a temperature high enough to melt the solder when it touches the work. Melting flux-cored solder on the soldering iron will usually destroy the effectiveness of the flux.

Soldering Repairs And Tips

Soldering tips are made of copper for good heat conductivity, but must be 'tinned' regularly for quick transfer of heat to the project and to prevent the solder from sticking to the iron. To tin the iron, simply heat it and touch the flux-cored solder to the tip; the solder will flow over the hot tip. Wipe the excess off with a clean rag, or use a damp sponge, but be careful — the iron will be hot.

After some use, the tip may be-

come pitted. If so, simply dress the tip smooth with a smooth file and tin the tip again. Flux-cored solder will remove oxides. However, rust, bits of insulation, oil and grease must be removed with a wire brush or emery cloth. For maximum strength in soldered parts, the joint must start off clean and tight. Weak joints will result if there are gaps too wide for the solder to bridge.

If a separate soldering flux is used, it should be brushed or swabbed only on areas that are to be soldered. Most solders contain a core of flux, therefore making separate fluxing unnecessary. Hold the work to be soldered firmly. It is best to solder on a wooden board, because a metal vise will only rob the piece to be soldered of heat and make it difficult to melt the solder.

Hold the soldering tip with the broadest face against the work to be soldered. Apply solder under the tip close to the work, using enough solder to give a heavy film between the iron and the piece being soldered, while moving slowly and making sure the solder melts properly. Keep the work level or the solder will run to the lowest part and favor the thicker parts, because these require more heat to melt the solder.

If the soldering tip overheats (i.e., the solder coating on the face of the top burns up), it should be retinned. Once the soldering is completed, let the soldered joint stand until cool to the touch. Seal all soldered wire splices with tape or heat shrink tubing after the repair has cooled.

Ignition System Diagnosis And Repair

IGNITION SYSTEM DESCRIPTION AND OPERATION

There are two kinds of ignition systems, Distributor Ignition (DI) and distributorless Electronic Ignition (EI).

All ignition systems are divided into two circuits, the primary and secondary. The primary circuit, or low voltage ignition circuit, is common to DI and EI systems and includes the battery, the ignition switch, the primary windings of the ignition coil(s), and a triggering mechanism (pick-up coil and reluctor, magnet and shutter vanes or slotted disc and photo optical sensor) and switching device to turn the circuit on and off.

With DI systems, the secondary system consists of the secondary windings of the ignition coil, the coil wire, the distributor cap and rotor, the spark plug wires, and the spark plugs.

EI systems have no distributor and instead have a coil for each cylinder or pair of cylinders. These coils are either directly connected to the spark plugs or are connected to them with conventional spark plug wires.

Current flows from the battery, through the ignition switch, through the coil primary, and through the switching device to ground.

Functionally, the ignition coil is a transformer and its primary side is wound with about 200 turns of relatively heavy wire. When the circuit is closed and current is flowing through the primary circuit, a powerful magnetic field builds up on the coil's primary windings.

The secondary windings, which usually sit inside the primary windings, consist of about 22,000 turns of very fine wire. When the circuit

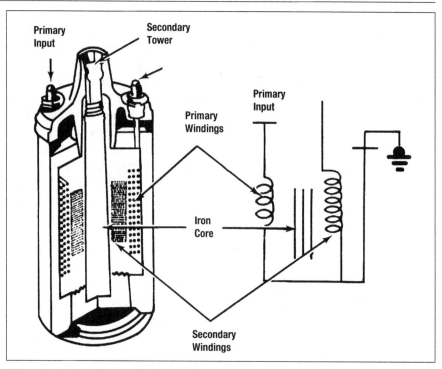

Internal construction and schematic of a conventional oil-filled coil.

is opened by the switching device (the ignition control module and/or PCM/ECM), primary current stops flowing. Then the energy stored in the primary windings collapses across the secondary windings, inducing a voltage in them. Depending upon how the primary system and the coil are designed, secondary voltage potential can range from 25,000 to 50,000 volts. Some modern systems produce 80,000 volts.

On DI systems, the secondary voltage goes out through the coil's secondary terminal, through the coil wire to the distributor cap center terminal, from the center terminal to the rotor spring arm, across the rotor to one of the distributor cap terminals, through the plug wire to the spark plug, and the plug fires. As the distributor turns, the rotor distributes the voltage from the coil to each distributor terminal in the vehicle's firing order.

On EI systems the coils are signaled to fire in the proper order by the ignition control module and/or PCM/ECM, which also controls the spark timing and advance.

IGNITION SYSTEM INSPECTION

Overall, ignition systems suffer from the same problems that afflict any electrical circuit. They are hurt by high resistance connections, open circuits, wire-to-wire shorts, and shorts to ground. In addition, they are often damaged by the same things that hurt electronic circuits: reversed polarities, and static discharges. Such problems cause weak spark or no spark at the spark plugs. The result is symptoms such as no-start, hard start, misfire or stumble under acceleration. When troubleshooting an ignition system, always check for DTCs related to ignition system operation.

Perform a visual inspection of the

ignition wiring and components. Make sure the spark plug wires are securely connected to the spark plugs, distributor cap and/or coil(s). Inspect the wires and wire boots for wear and cracking and replace as necessary. Check that the firing order is correct on DI systems and make sure that wires from consecutively firing cylinders cross rather than run parallel, to prevent crossfiring. Check the coil(s) for cracks, carbon tracking, oil leakage or other damage.

Check the primary circuit wiring for damage, corrosion and poor connections, which can cause voltage drops. If there is an intermittent problem, you may have to wiggle or gently tug on the wiring, including the connection at the ignition switch, with the engine running to find the cause.

Damaged or worn out distributor caps and rotors can cause a variety of problems, such as a no start condition, hard starting, missing, lack of power, rough idle, high emissions, and poor fuel economy. Inspect the distributor cap for cracks, wear or other damage. Check the spark plug wire and coil wire terminals for corrosion. Check the locating tab and hold-downs to make sure the cap is secured properly to the distributor.

Remove the distributor cap and check the rotor contact terminals for wear, corrosion or other damage. Look for cracks or evidence of carbon tracking. A carbon track is a small line of carbon that conducts electricity. A carbon track can cause coil voltage to short to ground or to the wrong plug wire, causing a misfire or causing a plug to fire at the wrong time.

Inspect the rotor for cracks, carbon tracks and erosion or other damage to the rotor tip and spring arm contact. Check the rotor locating tab and hold-downs to make sure the rotor is properly positioned on the distributor shaft. Remove the rotor and look for discoloration in the center at the

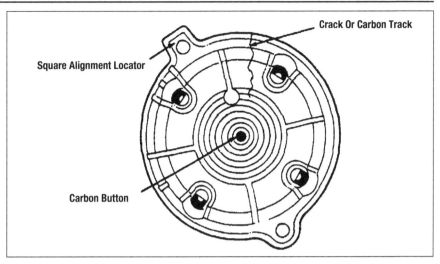

Typical location for crack or carbon track in a distributor cap. *(Courtesy: Ford Motor Co.)*

top and bottom. Such discoloration is evidence of 'rotor burn through'; indicating the high voltage from the coil has burned through the rotor and is grounding on the distributor shaft.

Inspect the condition of the triggering mechanism and wiring. These components are inside the distributor on DI systems and mounted on the engine near the crankshaft on EI systems. The triggering mechanism components seldom require service, although the pickup air gap can be adjusted on some systems. A non-magnetic feeler gauge must be used when checking the gap between the pickup and the tips of the reluctor wheel. Try to move the distributor shaft from side-to-side to check the condition of the distributor bushings before performing this adjustment. Excessive play could change the pickup gap and cause a misfire.

IGNITION SYSTEM DIAGNOSIS

The following are common problems and possible ignition system related causes:

No Start or Hard Start
- low or no primary voltage at the coil
- defective coil
- open coil wire

- defective distributor cap and/or rotor
- defective triggering mechanism
- defective ignition module
- fouled spark plugs

Engine Misfire
- low primary voltage
- defective coil
- defective distributor cap and/or rotor
- worn distributor
- high resistance in spark plug wires
- incorrectly routed spark plug wires
- defective spark plugs

Power Loss
- defective coil
- late ignition timing
- not enough timing advance
- engine misfire

Spark Knock
- spark plug heat range too hot
- incorrectly routed spark plug wires
- ignition timing too far advanced

Poor Mileage
- engine misfire
- late ignition timing
- not enough timing advance

No-Start Diagnosis

If the vehicle will not start because of a no-spark condition, then perform the following tests.

Connect a 12-volt test light to the coil negative terminal and ground, then turn the ignition key to the ON position. The test light should be on. If not there is an open in the coil primary windings or in the circuit from the ignition switch to the coil battery terminal.

Watch the test light while cranking the engine. If the light flickers, the signal from the pickup coil and module are OK. If the light does not flicker when the engine is cranked, test the pickup coil with an ohmmeter. If the pickup coil tests OK, then

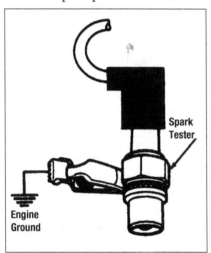

Typical spark tester.

the module is defective.

If the test light flickered, disconnect the coil wire from the distributor cap and connect a spark tester to the wire. Ground the tester and crank the engine. If the spark tester fires, the ignition coil is OK. If the spark tester does not fire, then the coil is defective.

The spark tester can be used at each of the spark plug wires. If the tester then fails to fire when the engine is cranked, there is a problem with the spark plug wire, distributor cap or rotor.

Performance Diagnosis With A Scope

An oscilloscope converts the electrical signals from the ignition system into a visual image showing voltage changes over a period of time. This voltage line is called a pattern. The technician can study these patterns and compare with known good ones to determine what is happening in the ignition system.

The primary scope pattern shows the low voltage changes in the primary circuit of the ignition system. However, since the secondary ignition circuit is dependent upon a properly functioning primary circuit, and any primary circuit problems are reflected in the secondary circuit, it is the secondary scope pattern that is checked more often.

The secondary scope pattern has three sections: firing, intermediate and dwell. The firing section starts on the left side of the screen. Problems with the spark plugs, plug wires, distributor cap and rotor will be indi-

cated here.

The firing section begins with the firing line. The firing line represents the amount of voltage required to jump the spark plug gap. The firing line should be 7-13kV, with no more than 3kV variation between cylinders. Once the spark has been initiated, a horizontal line will be displayed about three quarters of the way down on the firing line. This is called the spark line. The burn voltage is the height on the voltage scale of the spark line. The burn voltage indicates the amount of energy required to sustain the flow of current across the plug electrodes.

The intermediate section shows a series of diminishing oscillations that represents residual coil energy. This residual energy gradually dissipates between the switching device and coil. Problems with the ignition coil(s) will be indicated in this section.

The dwell section begins when the switching device turns on to allow

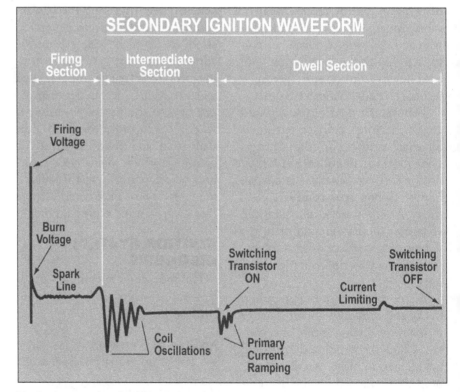

Typical secondary ignition scope pattern.

current flow to the ignition coil. There should be a short downward drop followed by small oscillations. The dwell section is where the magnetic field builds up in the ignition coil. Problems with the triggering mechanism and ignition module will be indicated in this section.

An oscilloscope can display patterns in different ways for diagnostic purposes. The patterns for all cylinders can be superimposed (placed on top of one another) to check for uniformity. Any pattern that does not align with the others can indicate a problem with that cylinder. For example, if one cylinder has a firing line and burn time that is different from the other cylinders, there is most likely a problem with the spark plug or spark plug wire in that cylinder.

Patterns can also be lined up in a parade display, where the pattern for each cylinder is shown side by side. This display is useful for comparing firing voltages. Tall firing lines indicate high resistance while short firing lines indicate low resistance.

The raster, or stacked display places all cylinder patterns on top of one another. This display is used to check timing or dwell variations between cylinders.

COMPONENT TESTING

Ignition Switch

A defective ignition switch or ignition switch wiring may not allow enough power to the ignition module or ignition coil. The switch can be tested with a Digital Multimeter (DMM).

Ground the negative lead of the DMM to the distributor base. With the ignition switch in the OFF position, connect the positive lead to the power wire at the module. Turn the ignition switch to the run or start position, as required, and measure the voltage. The voltage reading should be at least 90% of battery voltage.

Ignition Coils

Ignition coils have advanced beyond the conventional cylindrical type of coil that was used for many years. Today there are four types of ignition coils: external, which covers the conventional coils as well, internal, EI system (distributorless) waste spark ignition coils and direct ignition Coil On Plug (COP) coils. The external coil is referred to as such because, depending on the manufacturer, the coil will be located either on the engine, firewall or strut tower (anywhere outside the distributor).

The second type is the internal ignition coil, which is located inside or is a part of the distributor cap or distributor. The GM High Energy Ignition (HEI) system ignition coil is an internal type coil, because it is located within the distributor cap.

The third type of coil is the EI system waste spark ignition coil. These coils usually come as a two- or three-pack depending on the number of cylinders the engine has. One coil provides spark for two cylinders. For example, a 4-cylinder engine would have two coils in a pack and a 6 cylinder would have three coils in a pack. The coils are grouped according to companion cylinders—cylinders whose pistons are at TDC at the same time. The spark plug fires in each cylinder simultaneously, but most of the available energy goes to the cylinder that is on the compression stroke, the 'event' cylinder, because there is little resistance from the other cylinder, which is on the exhaust stroke.

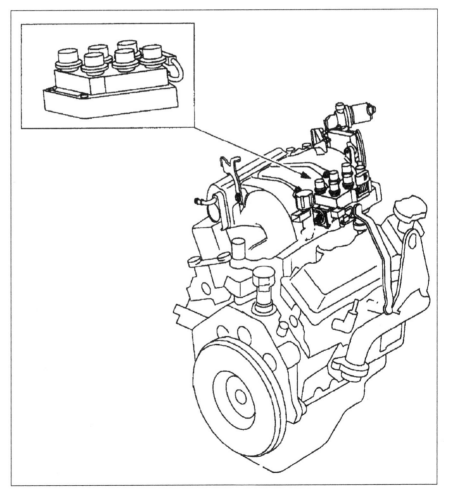

Typical distributorless waste spark EI system coil pack on a 6-cylinder engine. (Courtesy: Ford Motor Co.)

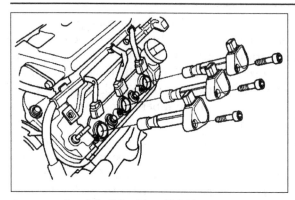

An example of Coil On Plug (COP) ignition coils.
(Courtesy: Honda Motor Co., Ltd.)

The last type of coil, the COP coil, is used in a distributorless system where the coil is mounted directly to the spark plugs. Secondary resistance is minimized with this design because the spark plug wires have been eliminated.

In any event, each type of ignition coil performs the same function: to convert a low primary voltage (battery) into a high secondary voltage and supply that voltage to the spark plug.

Test ignition coil resistance using an ohmmeter. To measure primary resistance, connect the ohmmeter leads to the positive and negative terminals. Measure secondary resistance by connecting the leads to the nega-

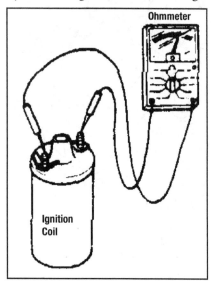

Measuring ignition coil primary resistance with an ohmmeter.
(Courtesy: Ford Motor Co.)

tive terminal and high tension wire terminal. A basic primary coil resistance for DI system coils should be approximately 0.5 to 15 ohms; the secondary side will range between 800 to 10,000 ohms. For EI system coils resistance will be slightly lower: the primary resistance will range between 0.2 to 2.0 ohms. The secondary side would typically fall between 4,000 to 7,000 ohms. Consult the vehicle service manual for specifications.

Resistance tests may not always determine if a coil is faulty. Careful visual inspection of the coil and testing of the ignition system under load may be the only accurate way of ascertaining if a coil is defective. Some defects will only reveal themselves during scope testing.

Coils usually used on distributorless systems are designed to fit mechanically one way. Sometimes, the electrical leads in coil packs are color coded, and must be replaced one wire at a time to ensure that the leads do not become misplaced. On older systems and new, remember to respect the intended polarity of the ignition coil during replacement. Using the 'one wire at a time' method will help to prevent problems.

Bad wires are the prime causes of coil failure on modern engines. They create either a low resistance short or a high resistance open. A low resistance wire insulation, which allows spark voltage to flow to ground, causes a miss and makes the coil overheat, shortening its life. An open wire (high resistance) forces the coil to find an alternative path to ground, often through the coil case, ruining the integrity of the unit and bleeding coil energy to ground. If the module is mounted below the coils, it may be damaged as the energy finds its way to ground. Always check your wires

when replacing coils for this reason.

Primary Circuit Triggering

Various methods are used to turn the primary circuit on and off:

Distributor Pick-Up Coils

The distributor pick-up coil is better known as a magnetic pick-up coil assembly, or stator. There are different designs. On some designs, the pick-up contains a permanent magnet, a pole piece with internal teeth and a pick-up coil. A rotating timer core is used with this type. On others, it contains a permanent magnet and a single tooth pick-up coil. A reluctor or armature is used with this type. Some use a photocell, Light Emitting Diode (LED) and a wheel with slits to provide an rpm signal to a light sensitive photoreceptor.

The more common magnetic pick-up coil design will be described. When the teeth of the rotating timer core and pole piece align, or the reluctor and the single tooth of the pick-up, an induced voltage in the pick-up coil signals the electronic module to open the coil primary circuit. As the primary current decreases, a high voltage is induced in the secondary winding of the ignition coil, directing a spark through the rotor, which in turn fires the spark plugs. The pick-up coil is located inside the ignition distributor.

Before testing, check to see if spark is evident. If there is spark, the pick-up assembly is not the problem.

To test the pick-up coil, first disconnect the pick-up coil electrical leads from the module. Set the ohmmeter on the high scale. Connect one lead of the ohmmeter to ground and probe each lead of the pick-up coil connector. For this test, any resistance measurement less than infinity requires the replacement of the pick-up coil.

Pick-up coil continuity is tested using an ohmmeter (on low range) between the pick-up coil connector leads. Normal resistance is 500 to 1500 ohms. Use the specifications for the unit you are testing. If a vacuum unit is used, move the vacuum advance arm while performing this test. This will detect any break in coil continuity. Such a condition can cause intermittent misfiring. Replace the pick-up coil if the reading is outside the specified limits.

If no defects have been found at this time, and a problem still exists, the module will need to be checked.

On some distributors, the pickup coil gap requires adjustment, however usually only when components are replaced. The gap between the pick-up coil and reluctor must be adjusted using a non-magnetic feeler gauge. Pick-up coil gap that is too small or too large may cause engine misfire. A larger than specified gap may also keep the engine from starting.

Hall Effect Triggering

Hall Effect ignition triggering is similar to the magnetic-impulse design. However, where the magnetic-impulse voltage signal is a speed-sensitive AC pulse, the Hall effect uses a clean square-wave signal that remains constant regardless of engine speed. Only the width of the pulse changes with rpm.

Placing metal or a magnet near the system and then removing it, which makes the system change from one voltage to another, accomplishes signal switching. For example, one Hall system produces a square wave pattern that switches between 12 volts and 0 volts.

You can test a Hall effect system with a DMM (Digital Multimeter) and/or an oscilloscope. Procedures vary, however, so always consult the appropriate service manual before you test a Hall effect triggering device.

Crankshaft Position Sensor (CKP)

EI systems also use permanent magnet generator or Hall effect trig-

gering. However, the reluctor component or Hall-triggering component is

a gear-shaped wheel mounted on the crankshaft.

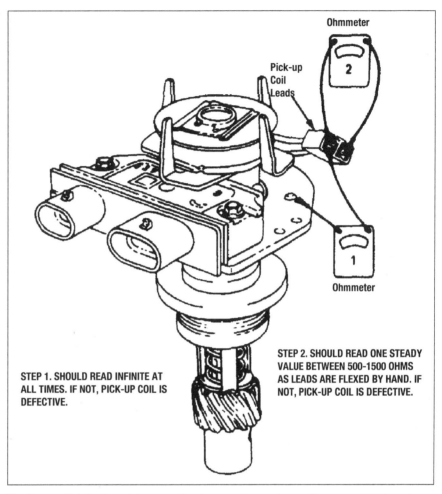

STEP 1. SHOULD READ INFINITE AT ALL TIMES. IF NOT, PICK-UP COIL IS DEFECTIVE.

STEP 2. SHOULD READ ONE STEADY VALUE BETWEEN 500-1500 OHMS AS LEADS ARE FLEXED BY HAND. IF NOT, PICK-UP COIL IS DEFECTIVE.

Testing a distributor pick-up coil using an ohmmeter. *(Courtesy: GM Corp.)*

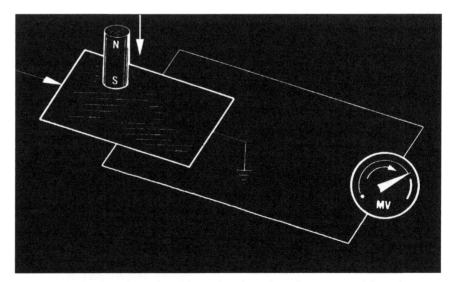

If current is flowing through a thin wafer of semiconductor material, and a magnetic field crosses it at a right angle, a voltage known as a Hall effect voltage will be generated at the edge of the material. Interrupting the magnetic field turns off the voltage. This is the principle used by Hall effect sensors

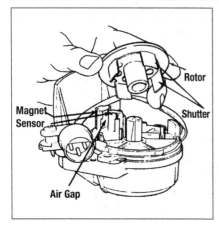

On this Hall effect ignition trigger, the shutter vanes on the distributor's rotor pass between a permanent magnet and the Hall sensor, causing the sensor to change states repeatedly. Regardless of rpm, Hall sensors produce consistent square-wave patterns of equal height (voltage)

Some crankshaft triggering components have one tooth per engine cylinder; others have as many as 36 teeth. The greater number of teeth improves the frequency and accuracy of the triggering signal.

Depending on engine design, the pickup coil or Hall effect sensor may be located in its own receptacle inside the engine block. On other engines, you may find the pickup coil or Hall effect sensor mounted on an external bracket near the crankshaft.

Both permanent magnet and Hall effect sensors can be diagnosed using a scope. The typical pattern for a magnetic sensor is shown in the accompanying illustration. The pattern will vary according to the position and number of slots machined into the trigger wheel. The wheel shown has nine slots. Eight are evenly spaced with the ninth right next to one of the eight. This slot is for the synch pulse. On some systems a CMP (Camshaft Position Sensor) is used instead of a synch pulse from the CKP.

The triggering signal is the almost instantaneous drop from maximum positive voltage to maximum neg-

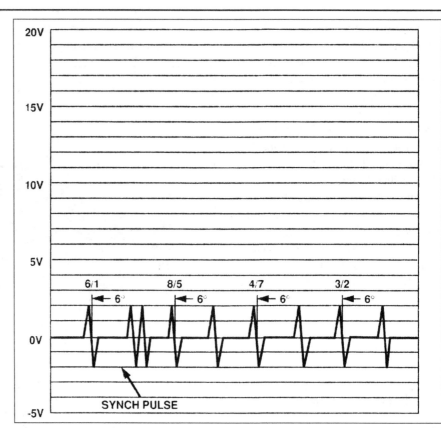

Typical permanent magnet generator crankshaft sensor waveform. *(Courtesy: GM Corp.)*

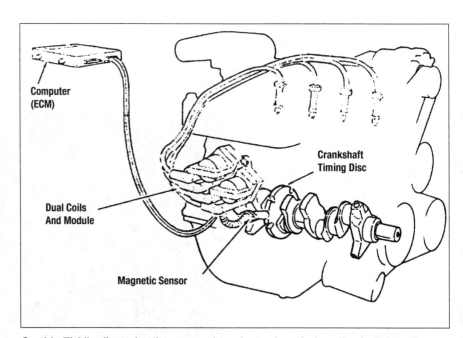

On this EI (distributorless) system, the reluctor is a timing disc built into the center of the crankshaft. As the disc's notches pass by the tip of the PM (permanent magnet) sensor, an AC voltage pulse is generated in the shape of a sine-waveform. This system is polarity sensitive, so if you replace the harness connector be certain the wires don't get reversed. In that case, the engine will only crank and produce no spark

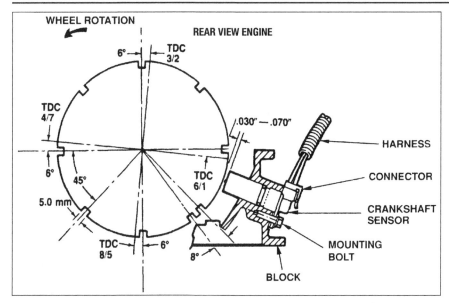

Typical permanent magnet generator crankshaft sensor.   *(Courtesy: GM Corp.)*

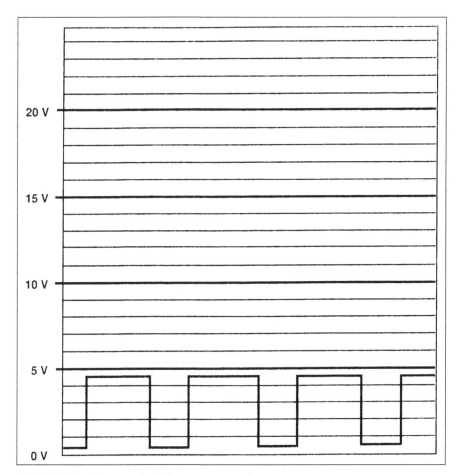

Typical Hall effect crankshaft sensor waveform.   *(Courtesy: GM Corp.)*

ative voltage. Low amplitude (low voltage) from the CKP sensor, which can cause a no-start condition, may indicate a weak magnet or a spacing problem with relation to the crankshaft.

A typical Hall effect sensor pattern is shown in the accompanying illustration. Each pulse should be identical in shape, amplitude and spacing. The top of the trace represents the feed voltage; a clean solid line here indicates a good power source. When the sensor turns on, the voltage drops to zero. The downward and upward lines should be straight. If the upward line rises at an angle, the voltage is rising too slowly, which could cause a no-start condition.

The relationship between the CKP sensor and the ignition module can be seen on a dual trace scope. A fixed amount of timing advance is used for starting purposes. This is the result of where the notches are physically machined.

Electronic Ignition Module

The ignition module fires the ignition coil after the magnetic pick-up coil submits an electrical pulse or signal to it. The ignition module interrupts the ignition primary circuit, thus causing the ignition coil to provide spark. The ignition module turns the ignition coil on and off, like mechanical ignition points did on older vehicles. The ignition module turns off the primary circuit to the coil that begins the induction of the magnetic lines of force from the primary side of the coil into the secondary side of the coil. This induction provides spark to the spark plugs.

The advantages of this system are that the transistors in the control unit can make and break the primary ignition circuit much faster than ignition points can, and higher primary voltage can be utilized, since this system is designed to handle higher voltage without adverse effects. On earlier systems, the ignition module governed the ignition dwell, whereas on later systems the PCM/ECM controls dwell.

Due to the many styles and configurations of ignition modules, there is no one easy test that will work universally. However, several steps can be taken to determine whether the ignition module is defective.

First, check for spark at the spark plug wire. This can be done using a spark tester, which looks like a regular spark plug with a ground clip attached to one side. It allows the ignition system to be checked for spark without damaging the electronics. If the engine is getting spark, the ignition module is most probably functioning correctly. Testing the ignition system for spark without the use of a spark tester can damage the ignition module.

If the engine is not getting spark, check the ignition coil, ignition trigger (usually a magnetic reluctance or Hall effect switch) and all associated wiring. If all other components are functioning properly, the ignition module is probably defective. As a final test, an ignition module tester may be used to check the module circuitry. A handheld tester for the TFI family of ignition is very valuable for time saved and accuracy of diagnosis.

A simple test involves the use of a test light or logic probe. Locate the ignition coil in the engine compartment. On some ignition systems, the coil is located inside the distributor cap. Connect a test light or logic probe between the negative side of the coil and ground. Crank the engine using the starter motor. As the engine cranks the test light or logic probe bulb should flicker. This indicates the module is triggering the coil to fire. If the light does not flicker, the module is most likely at fault. Be certain you have eliminated the power up circuit and the ground as a cause of module failure.

Secondary Circuit Components

Problems with spark plug wires and spark plugs are most easily seen on an engine analyzer or oscilloscope. Wires with excessively high resistance will be indicated by an abnormally high firing line on a scope pattern. The resistance of suspect wires can be checked using an ohmmeter.

Check spark plugs for appearance and spark plug gap. The spark plug electrodes should be squared off and the insulator should be a light tan.

Check spark plug gap using a wire gauge and bend the side electrode to adjust to specification. A gap that is too tight will cause a lower firing voltage resulting in incomplete combustion. If the gap is too wide, the coil may not generate enough voltage to bridge the gap for the required time.

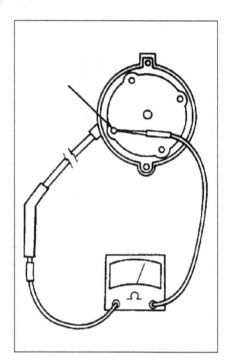

Checking the resistance of a spark plug wire using an ohmmeter. *(Courtesy: Ford Motor Co.)*

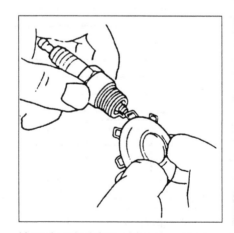

Keep in mind that wider plug gaps are just one of several factors that can increase the level of required firing (secondary) voltage; narrower gaps reduce required voltage

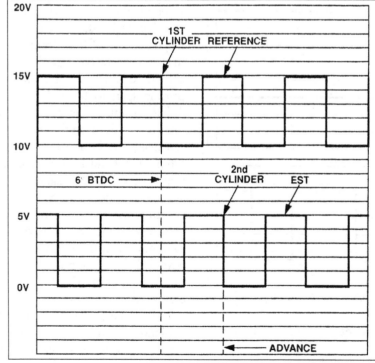

EST and crankshaft sensor signals. *(Courtesy: GM Corp.)*

Gap Bridged

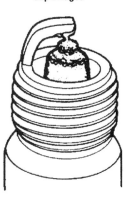

Identified by deposit build-up closing gap between electrodes. Caused by oil or carbon fouling. Replace plug, or if deposits are not excessive, the plug can be cleaned.

Oil Fouled

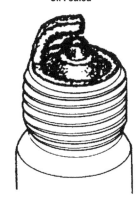

Identified by wet deposits on the insulator shell bore electrodes. Caused by excessive oil entering combustion chamber through worn rings and pistons. Excessive clearance between valve guides or worn or loose bearings. Correct oil problem. Replace the plug.

Carbon Fouled

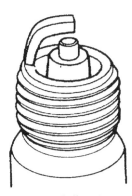

Identified by black, dry fluffy carbon deposits on insulator tips, exposed shell surfaces and electrodes.
Caused by too cold a plug, weak ignition, dirty air cleaner, defective fuel pump, too rich a fuel mixture, improperly operating heat riser or excessive idling. Can be cleaned.

Normal

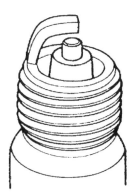

Identified by light tan or gray deposits on the firing tip.

Pre-Ignition

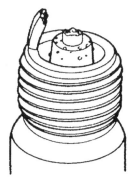

Identified by melted electrodes and possibly blistered insulator. Metallic deposits on insulator indicate engine damage.
Caused by wrong type of fuel, incorrect ignition timing or advance, too hot a plug, burnt valves or engine overheating. Replace the plug.

Overheating

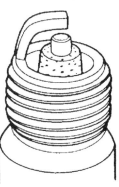

Identified by a white or light gray insulator with small black or gray brown spots and with bluish-burnt appearance of electrodes.
Caused by engine overheating, wrong type of fuel, loose spark plugs, too hot a plug, low fuel pump pressure or incorrect ignition timing. Replace the plug.

Fused Spot Deposit

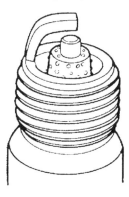

Identified by melted or spotty deposits resembling bubbles or blisters.
Caused by sudden acceleration. Can be cleaned if not excessive, otherwise, replace the plug.

Spark plug diagnosis chart

Notes

Fuel, Air Induction And Exhaust Systems Diagnosis And Repair

FUEL DELIVERY SYSTEM

An insufficient amount of fuel delivered to the engine can cause a no-start condition or a lean mixture. Low fuel pressure can be caused by a clogged fuel filter, a defective pressure regulator or a restricted fuel line.

Excessive fuel pressure can cause a rich mixture. High fuel pressure can be caused by a restricted fuel return line or a defective pressure regulator.

WARNING: Fuel injection systems remain under pressure, even after the engine has been turned OFF. The fuel system pressure must be relieved before disconnecting any fuel lines. Failure to do so may result in fire and/or personal injury.

System Inspection

Inspect the general condition of the fuel system. Look for dented, damaged or corroded lines, cracked or swollen hoses and leaks. Make sure all connections are secure and all lines and hoses are securely mounted so they can't rub against other components.

Check the fuel tank for damage and leaks, and make sure it is securely mounted. Inspect the hoses, lines and wiring at the tank, making sure they

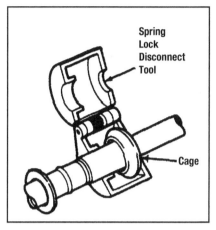

A special tool for separating spring-lock fittings. Always check the spring in this type of fitting prior to reassembly and replace if missing or damaged.
(Courtesy: Ford Motor Co.)

are properly connected. Make sure the fuel tank neck and cap are secure.

When replacing a fuel line, use only steel tubing, never copper, and make sure the line is properly attached to the frame. When replacing fuel hoses, make sure they are approved for fuel system use.

Fuel lines and components are connected using various types of fittings, many of which require special tools to disconnect. If specified, always use the special tool to prevent damaging fittings and fuel sys-

tem components. Many fittings use O-rings, which should never be reused. Always replace O-rings with those specified for fuel system use.

When replacing an in-line fuel filter, first properly relieve the fuel system pressure and then position a drain pan under the filter to catch any spilled fuel. Properly disconnect the fuel lines from the filter and remove the filter from its mounting. Make sure the new filter is installed in the proper fuel flow direction.

Relieving Fuel System Pressure

Fuel system pressure can be relieved in several ways. A special gauge with a drain hose can be attached to a Schrader valve on the fuel rail, with another hose from the gauge placed in a suitable container. A button on the gauge is then pressed to release the pressure and allow the fuel to drain into the container. Another way involves removing the fuel pump fuse, starting the engine and letting it run until it stalls. When in doubt as to what method to use, consult the vehicle service manual for the manufacturer's recommended procedure.

Alcohol Contamination

Oxygenated fuel that contains up to 10% alcohol (ethanol) is used in many areas of the U.S. So called 'flex fuel' vehicles have a sensor that detects the percentage of ethanol in the fuel and the system adjusts the air/fuel mixture accordingly, which allows them to use E85, which is 85% ethanol. However, most other vehicles cannot tolerate alcohol in fuel that exceeds 10%. If an excessive amount of alcohol is mixed with gasoline on these vehicles, it can degrade

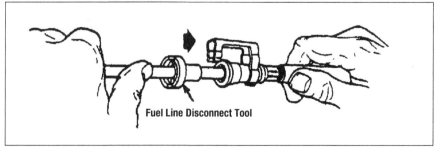

Using a special tool to disconnect a fuel line push-connect fitting.
(Courtesy: Ford Motor Co.)

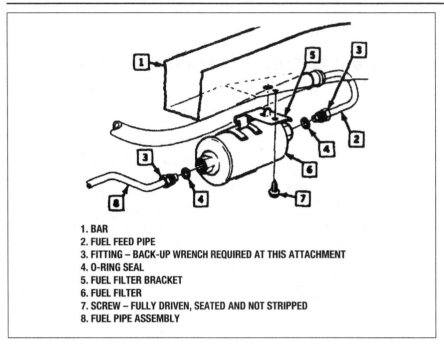

1. BAR
2. FUEL FEED PIPE
3. FITTING – BACK-UP WRENCH REQUIRED AT THIS ATTACHMENT
4. O-RING SEAL
5. FUEL FILTER BRACKET
6. FUEL FILTER
7. SCREW – FULLY DRIVEN, SEATED AND NOT STRIPPED
8. FUEL PIPE ASSEMBLY

When replacing fuel system components like this fuel filter, always use new O-rings designed for fuel system use. *(Courtesy: GM Corp.)*

rubber fuel system components, clog the fuel filter and cause a lean air/fuel mixture. These defects can cause a no-start condition, stalling and other driveability complaints.

If you suspect an excessive amount of alcohol in gasoline, fill a graduated 100mL container to the 90mL mark with the suspect gasoline. Add water to bring the level of the liquid to the 100mL mark. Close the container and shake vigorously for 10-15 seconds, then allow the contents to settle. Any alcohol that is in the gasoline will be absorbed by the water and settle to the bottom of the container. For example, if there is now 20mL of water, there was 10% alcohol in the gasoline.

There are commercially available test kits that perform this test. Be aware that this test will not remove all of the alcohol from the gasoline, so the percentage of alcohol in the gas may be higher than indicated.

Fuel Pump Volume and Pressure Tests

An engine that misfires or surges under heavy load or at higher speeds may be starved for fuel. An engine that will not start may have no fuel pressure. The traditional test sequence for any fuel pump is to check its volume first and pressure second.

First make sure there is an adequate amount of fuel in the tank. Just because the gauge reads a quantity of fuel, doesn't mean that enough fuel is present; the gauge or gauge sending unit could be defective.

Listen for noise from the pump when the key is turned on. If no noise is heard, check for voltage at the pump and check for excessive ground resistance using a DMM. If there is adequate voltage and the ground is good but the pump does not run, it is probably defective and should be replaced.

If there is no voltage when the key is on and the engine is cranking, check the pump fuse, relay and wiring. Sometimes an oil pressure switch is incorporated in the fuel pump circuit. Bypass the switch with a jumper wire; if there is now power to the pump, replace the switch.

For a volume test, disconnect the fuel pressure feed line and insert it into a graduated container. On systems with electric fuel pumps, you usually must operate the pump with a jumper wire for a specified period. It should flow at least a half-pint of fuel in 30 seconds. If not, before condemning the pump, check the external and in-tank fuel filters and the fuel lines for restriction. Also, perform a voltage drop test on the power and ground circuits to the pump.

If fuel delivery volume is OK, reconnect the pressure feed line, con-

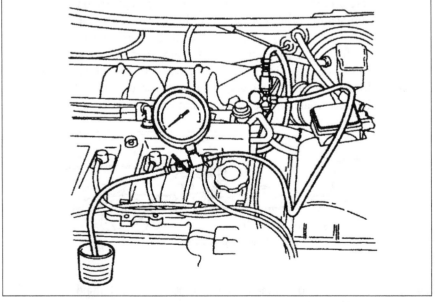

Checking fuel delivery volume *(Courtesy: Ford Motor Co.)*

nect a suitable pressure gauge and turn the key to the ON position. Compare the pressure reading with specifications. Pressure that is lower than specifications could be caused by a restricted filter, a faulty fuel pump or a faulty pressure regulator. Pressure that is higher than specifications could be caused by a faulty pressure regulator or a restricted fuel return line.

If the pressure is within specifications, wait five minutes while watching for a considerable pressure drop. If a drop occurs, block off the return line from the pressure regulator and recycle the key. If the pressure now holds, you have a defective regulator. If the pressure still drops, block off the feed line from the fuel pump and recycle the key. If the pressure holds steady, the fuel pump check valve is leaking and the pump must be replaced. If there is still a pressure drop and there are no external leaks, suspect one or more injectors of leaking.

If fuel pressure was OK and there was no pressure drop, start the engine and let it idle. With the vacuum line connected to the fuel pressure regulator, fuel pressure should be lower than with the line disconnected. If not, disconnect the vacuum line from the pressure regulator and apply vacuum to the regulator (consult the vehicle service manual for the specified amount). If the fuel pressure drops slightly, then there is a problem with

the vacuum source to the regulator. If the fuel pressure does not drop, the fuel pressure regulator is faulty.

Fuel Pump Replacement

Most electric fuel pumps are installed in the fuel tank and are incorporated with the fuel gauge sending unit, however there are some vehicles that use external electric fuel pumps mounted on the frame.

Tank-Mounted Pumps

Properly relieve the fuel system pressure. If fuel tank removal is necessary to gain access to the pump, drain or siphon the fuel from the tank, then support the tank and disconnect all wiring, lines and hoses from the tank. Remove the fuel tank fasteners and lower the tank from the vehicle.

Clean the area around the pump

opening to prevent dirt from entering the tank. Remove the bolts or retaining ring and remove the pump from the fuel tank. Install the new pump using a new seal. Raise the tank into position, as required, and secure the tank with the fasteners. Connect all lines, hoses and electrical connectors. Fill the tank with fuel, turn the key to the ON position to pressurize the fuel system and check for leaks.

Frame-Mounted Pumps

Properly relieve the fuel system pressure and then position a drain pan under the fuel pump to catch any spilled fuel. Remove any covers or other components, as necessary, to gain access to the fuel pump. Disconnect all lines, hoses and wiring from the fuel pump, remove the fuel pump fasteners and remove the fuel pump

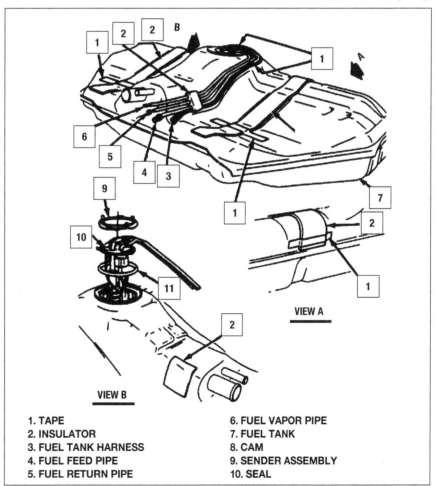

VIEW A

VIEW B

1. TAPE	6. FUEL VAPOR PIPE
2. INSULATOR	7. FUEL TANK
3. FUEL TANK HARNESS	8. CAM
4. FUEL FEED PIPE	9. SENDER ASSEMBLY
5. FUEL RETURN PIPE	10. SEAL

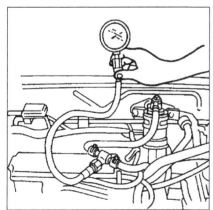

Checking fuel pressure
(Courtesy: Ford Motor Co.)

Typical fuel tank and fuel pump installation. *(Courtesy: GM Corp.)*

from the vehicle.

Place the new fuel pump in position and secure it with the fasteners. Connect the lines, hoses and wiring, as required. Install any components or covers that were removed. Turn the ignition key to the ON position to pressurize the fuel system and check for leaks.

FUEL INJECTION

There are two types of fuel injection: Throttle Body Injection (TBI) and Multiport Fuel Injection (MFI). On a TBI system, one or two injectors are located in a throttle body assembly that is mounted on a conventional intake manifold. The fuel is delivered above the throttle plates, mixes with air and is distributed to the intake ports by the intake manifold.

On an MFI system, the fuel is delivered to each intake port by individual injectors. The intake manifold in a multiport injection system is used only for air induction.

All TBI systems and most MFI systems are electrically operated. Sometimes, systems that use electrically operated injectors are generically called EFI or electronic fuel injection systems. One multiport system, the Bosch CIS (Continuous Injection System) uses hydraulically operated injectors. CIS injectors open at a pressure of about 35 to 45 psi. The CIS system is also known as the K-Jetronic system.

Electronic MFI systems can also be categorized according to injector firing strategy. Some early MFI systems fired their injectors in groups. Each injector in a group fired simultaneously and each group fired alternately. However, in a Sequential Fuel Injection (SFI) system, each injector is fired one at a time in the engine's spark plug firing order. All newer vehicles use the SFI system.

Note that on any multiport injection system, air leaks around the injectors can cause rough idle, hesitation, backfiring and poor fuel economy.

Diagnosis

When troubleshooting the fuel injection system, always check for DTCs related to fuel system operation. Also, use a scan tool to check the short term and long term fuel trims under different conditions.

The Short Term Fuel Trim (SFT) and Long Term Fuel Trim (LFT) strategies monitor the oxygen sensor signal on OBD II vehicles. The information is used by the PCM/ECM to change the amount of fuel delivered to the cylinders during closed loop operation according to operating conditions.

During open loop, the PCM/ECM operates the fuel injectors at a preprogrammed pulse width. When the engine goes into closed loop, the injector pulse width is changed in response to the oxygen sensor signal to maintain the correct air/fuel mixture. A rich mixture will increase the voltage signal from the oxygen sensor, which will in turn decrease the SFT and shorten the injector pulse width. A lean mixture will decrease the voltage signal, increase the SFT and lengthen the injector pulse width.

Increase and decrease to the SFT are represented on the scan tool as values above and below the number one when the vehicle is in closed loop. An SFT value of 1.10 means the pulse width was lengthened by 10% and will be displayed as +10. An SFT of 0.90 means the pulse width was shortened by 10% and will be shown on the scan tool as −10.

The SFT is used to modify the LFT. The LFT is stored in the PCM/ECM's memory and is part of the basic injection duration calculation. The PCM/ECM will change the LFT if the SFT remains higher or lower for longer than expected.

If the SFT numbers go back and forth between positive and negative, above and below one, the fuel system is operating properly. Correspondingly, numbers that remain on either side of one indicate a problem. A vac-

uum leak, which would cause a lean condition, would result in a LFT above one. Leaking injectors, which would cause a rich condition, would result in a LFT below one.

The fuel trims should be checked under different conditions because trims that are OK at idle but correct for a lean condition at highway speeds could indicate low fuel volume or a fuel restriction. Fuel trims that correct for a rich condition at idle, but are OK at higher rpms, could indicate a leaking or sticking injector(s).

Fuel Injectors

When the solenoid inside a fuel injector is turned on, it lifts a valve off its seat and the injector sprays fuel. The solenoid coil inside an injector has two terminals. When the ignition is on, power is usually fed to one injector terminal. When the control computer wants the injector to spray, it grounds the other terminal, completing the circuit to ground.

The longer the computer grounds the injector, the longer the injector sprays. The longer the injector sprays, the richer the mixture becomes. The less the injector sprays, the leaner the mixture. Injector 'on' time, which is also known as injector pulse width, is usually measured in milliseconds (ms). Mechanical problems include stuck open, stuck closed and leaking injectors.

Fuel Injector Testing

When an EFI-equipped engine won't start, you can usually determine if the injectors or their circuits are at fault without using a lot of sophisticated equipment. Connect a high-impedance test light (a 'noid' light) across an injector's terminals and crank the engine. If the light blinks consistently while you're cranking the engine, you know that, electrically at least, the injector and its circuit are working properly.

If the test light doesn't light up,

check the circuit between the injector and its power source. If the light comes on but won't blink, the injector driver circuit back at the computer has shorted, or the computer isn't telling the injectors to operate. Check the resistance of the injector solenoid. Injector resistances are generally in a very narrow range, and low values draw too much current through the injector driver transistors, and can cause failure of these drivers. If these parts are working properly, and the computer is supposed to be operating the injectors, then the computer is bad, as the drivers are not repairable in the shop. Check all of the injector resistance values before installing the new computer. Most computer rebuilders have a checklist to follow to reduce the possibility of ruining the new unit with a defective output device, which will draw too much current through the drivers in the output section. Be certain there is no condition, such as a missing input pulse from cam or crank sensors, which might be causing the computer to refuse to ground the injectors in turn for operation.

Checking static resistance sometimes is not enough to prove that an injector is operating properly. For example, on multiport injectors that are group fired, the PCM/ECM has a driver for each bank or pair of injectors. A V8 with multiport would have one driver for cylinders 1,3,5,7 and another for cylinders 2,4,6,8. A 4 cylinder might have separate drivers for cylinders 1,2 and 3,4. Fuel is delivered on both the compression and exhaust strokes of the affected cylinders. It is easy to misdiagnose this type of system when attempting to locate the cause of a misfire condition.

Suppose we have a V6 with group fired injectors and we find cylinders No. 2 and No. 6 are misfiring. After careful testing, we pin it down to the injectors in those two cylinders not spraying a sufficient amount of fuel. This will create a lean condition in

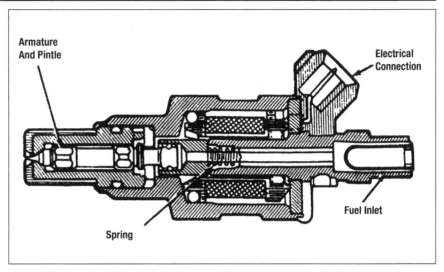

When the computer energizes the electromagnet inside a fuel injector, the magnet pulls the pintle off its seat, allowing the high-pressure fuel to spray out the end of the injector

cylinders No. 2 and No. 6. We reason that the PCM/ECM driver is OK as we have no problem with No. 4 cylinder. The resistance has been checked and is found to be in factory specification. However, after installing two new injectors the same problem remains.

What has happened here is that the injector with the least resistance is drawing most of the current when the circuit is energized. In this case,

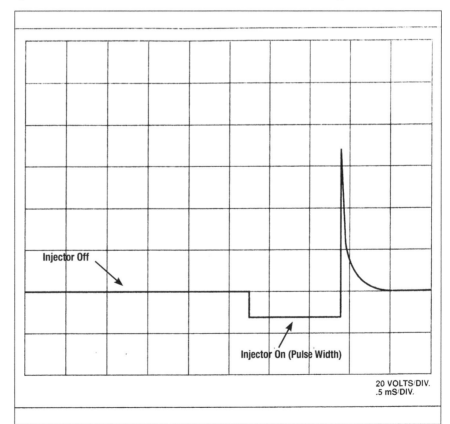

Typical fuel injector voltage pattern on an oscilloscope.
(Courtesy: GM Corp.)

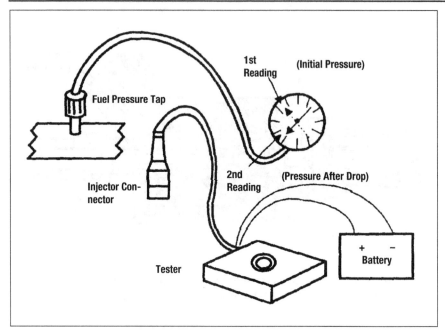

An example of an injector balance test. *(Courtesy: GM Corp.)*

No. 4 injector has low resistance, causing No. 2 and No. 6 cylinders to misfire by robbing current from its companion injectors.

But why did we not find this on the resistance test? Static resistance tests will generally pinpoint a shorted or open injector. However, many injectors will only short or draw excessive current when they are under load or stress. The problem in the V6 was diagnosed quickly and efficiently with a digital storage oscilloscope (DSO). The scope pattern produced a low voltage spike in the No. 4 injector.

Leaking injectors cause poor fuel economy, high emission levels, and a loss of rest pressure. In order to isolate the leaking injector, remove all the spark plugs, disable the ignition system and crank the engine until all fuel in the cylinders is removed. Allow the engine to sit for about 10 minutes. Turn the key ON and place the probe tip from your exhaust analyzer to each spark plug hole. Bump the starter to open the intake valve. An HC reading in any cylinder would indicate the presence of raw fuel. That's the cylinder with the leak-

ing injector.

Dirty or restricted fuel injectors tend to lean the mixture and cause rough idling, generally sluggish performance, poor fuel economy, and misfiring under load. To determine if the injectors are restricted, perform an injector balance test. Disconnect one injector and connect an injector balance tester and a fuel pressure gauge. Cycle the ignition key to the ON po-

sition. The gauge must hold pressure. In some vehicles, you may have to jumper the fuel pump relay (refer to the service manual), activate the tester and record the pressure drop. Repeat this test on all injectors, making sure that the starting pressure remains the same. Total the differences in pressure and divide by the number of injectors tested. Each injector's pressure drop should be within 1.5 psi of the average. To prevent flooding, the engine should be started between individual injector tests.

A larger drop in pressure indicates a leaking injector; less indicates a restricted one. An attempt to clean the injectors should be made and the test repeated, before any injectors are condemned.

Cold Start Injector

Fuel injection systems do not have chokes. Instead, they lengthen the injector pulse width for cold enrichment. Some fuel injection systems also improve cold start-up by using a separate injector called a cold-start injector. The cold-start injector sprays only during cranking when the engine is cold. Because the cold-start injector sprays only when the engine is cranking, it doesn't affect

SAMPLE INJECTOR BALANCE TEST

INJECTOR	STARTING PRESSURE	ENDING PRESSURE	DIFFERENCE
#1	44 psi	36 psi	8 psi
#2	44 psi	37 psi	7 psi
#3	44 psi	34 psi	10 psi
#4	44 psi	35 psi	9 psi
#5	44 psi	38 psi	6 psi
#6	44 psi	37 psi	7 psi

- Total of pressure drops = 47
  Average pressure drop = 7.8 psi
- Pressure drop acceptable range per injector = 6.3 to 9.3
- Injectors #3 and #5 fall outside of range.
  Clean and retest.

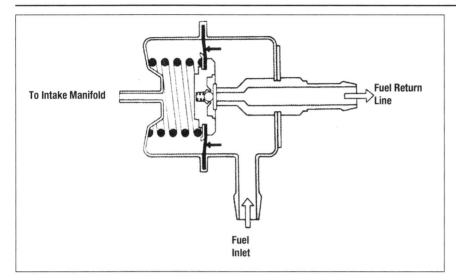

On most fuel injection systems, the fuel pressure regulator reacts to changes in manifold pressure (vacuum), which helps the regulator tailor the fuel pressure to engine load, and helps keep the fuel supplied to the injectors constant.

cold driveability.

Difficult cold starting often indicates a problem with the cold-start injector or with the circuit that controls it. Loss of rest pressure, poor fuel economy and high CO levels can indicate a leaking cold-start injector. Be certain that the switch that controls the cold injector passes its diagnostic tests before blaming the injector.

Fuel Pressure Regulator

Generally speaking, higher fuel pressure tends to make any TBI or port injection system run richer. Lower fuel pressure tends to make them run leaner.

A few fuel injection pressure regulators are adjustable; most of them are not. When fuel pressure is out-of-specification and the regulator is non-adjustable, you must replace the regulator.

Although they aren't externally adjustable, most fuel pressure regulators are connected to manifold vacuum and vary the fuel pressure according to engine load. Consequently, problems such as air leaks or a restricted vacuum sensing hose can upset the operation of a good pressure regulator.

When fuel pressure is too high, disconnect the fuel return line from the pressure regulator outlet. If disconnecting the return line brings the pressure down within specifications, you know there's a restriction somewhere in the return line. Some regulators can suffer from a ruptured diaphragm, allowing fuel to be sucked into the intake manifold through the vacuum line, which operates the regulator, causing a rich running condition. If you pull off the vacuum line from the regulator and find liquid fuel, replace the regulator.

Throttle Body

The throttle body on multiport fuel injected engines is susceptible to contamination that can restrict air flow and in turn cause idle speed problems. This contamination can be caused by dirt from a faulty air filtration system and by sludge buildup caused by the Positive Crankcase Ventilation (PCV) system.

The PCM/ECM bases idle speed calculations on a set amount of air that bypasses the throttle plates. If this air flow is reduced by accumulated deposits, these calculations will be incorrect and may result in stalling.

Sometimes these deposits can be cleaned off with a spray cleaner or wiped off with a cloth and solvent after the air duct is removed. However, if these methods prove ineffective, it may be necessary to remove the throttle body for more thorough cleaning.

Clean the throttle body with a soft brush and approved cleaning agent. Blow out the air passages with compressed air. Before submerging the throttle body in any kind of cleaner, components like the Throttle Position (TP) sensor and Idle Air Control (IAC) valve must be removed.

When reinstalling the throttle body, make sure all of the mounting surfaces are clean and use a new gasket. Torque the mounting bolts to specification. Adjust the TP sensor, as necessary.

This is a typical EFI fuel circuit. Most systems use a fuel pump submerged in fuel in the tank, and some have a second electric pump closer to the engine. Note how the fuel pressure regulator routes unused fuel back to the tank. A restriction in the return line can raise fuel pressure

Idle Control Devices

On most electronic fuel injected engines, engine idle speeds are controlled by the PCM/ECM through the Idle Air Control (IAC) valve. On most engines, the IAC valve is mounted on the throttle body; others may be mounted on the engine near the throttle body. IAC valves that are located on the throttle body operate as follows:

The PCM/ECM sends voltage pulses to the IAC motor windings causing the IAC motor shaft and pintle to move in or out a given distance (number of steps) for each pulse (called counts). The movement of the pintle controls the air flow around the throttle plate, which in turn controls engine idle speed. IAC valve pintle position counts can be ob-

served using a scan tool. Zero counts correspond to a fully closed passage, while 140 counts or more corresponds to full flow.

IAC valves that are mounted separately from the throttle body operate this way: Based on information the PCM/ECM receives from the coolant temperature sensor, intake air temperature sensor and throttle position sensor, it adjusts the opening of the IAC valve accordingly. When the engine is first started, it opens the IAC valve to its full amount. This causes the engine to run at a fast idle. As the engine temperature warms up the PCM/ECM signals the IAC valve to close and open, as increased air is needed. This maintains the idle speed at proper specification.

When suspecting an IAC valve problem, first perform a visual inspection. Most problems can be found in wiring harnesses and connectors. An unstable idle or stalling condition could be caused by a vacuum leak or faulty PCV valve. In some cases, just dirty electrical connections at the IAC valve can cause a problem. Proper diagnosis can only be accomplished by systematic testing procedures.

To test the IAC valve, begin with a cold engine. Start the engine. Using a voltmeter, check the voltage reading by probing the feed circuit to the IAC valve. Allow the engine to warm up while observing the voltmeter reading.

The initial reading should be high, close to battery voltage. As the engine warms up the

voltage reading should gradually decrease to almost 0 volts.

Another test that can be made is by checking the resistance between the terminals of the IAC valve for an open circuit, or checking the positive feed terminal to ground to see if the valve is shorted. These resistance values may vary, but should never be an open circuit.

CIS

As mentioned earlier, CIS is a mechanical port injection system. The CIS air flow sensing and mixture enrichment process, which appears on some older European vehicles, differs from EFI systems.

The CIS system has an air flow sensor plate mounted on a pivoted lever. As the engine draws in air, the sensor plate moves and the lever pivots with it. A device called the fuel distributor sits on the opposite end of the pivoted lever from the air sensor plate. As air flow moves the lever, the lever moves a valve in the center of the fuel distributor called the control plunger. The greater the air flow, the greater the control plunger travel and the more fuel the plunger allows each injector to have.

Fuel pressure, also called control pressure, balances movement of the control plunger. The air sensor lever works on one end of the plunger, and control pressure works on the other end. Remember, the greater the control pressure, the less the control plunger moves. And, the less the plunger moves, the less fuel flows to the injectors.

In short, high control pressure equals lean mixture, and vice versa.

Warm-Up Compensator

The warm-up compensator is a heated device that varies control pressure according to temperature. If a CIS-equipped engine runs poorly when cold, check control pressure. Control pressure should vary from a relatively low pressure (about 8 psi)

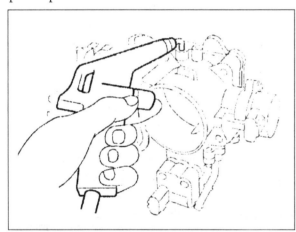

Cleaning a typical throttle body assembly.
(Courtesy: Toyota Motor Corp.)

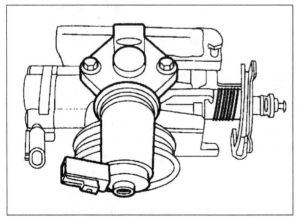

A Throttle body mounted IAC valve.
(Courtesy: Ford Motor Co.)

on a cold engine to a higher pressure (about 50 psi) when the engine warms up. When in doubt, refer to the compensator pressure/temperature chart in the service manual.

Be sure the warm-up compensator heater hasn't open-circuited, and that it has power going to it. Then, beginning with a cold start-up, watch control pressure as the engine warms up. Replace the warm-up compensator if the pressure falls out of the range shown on the pressure/temperature chart.

AIR INDUCTION SYSTEM

A dirty or clogged air filter will restrict air flow into the throttle body, possibly causing an overly rich air/fuel mixture and resulting in reduced engine performance, poor fuel economy and excessive HC and CO exhaust emissions. Remove the air filter from its housing and gently tap it on a hard surface to dislodge dirt. Visually inspect the filter for holes and other damage. Hold the filter up to a light source to check the filter. If the filter is clean, light will pass through all areas. Dark areas on a filter element will not allow light to pass through; the filter is dirty and must be replaced.

When replacing the filter element, wipe any dirt from the housing and make sure the filter seals fit properly.

Check and replace the crankcase breather filter. Check the air intake ducting for cracks and poor joint sealing that could allow air into the engine other than through the filter. This is especially important on vehicles with remote mounted MAF (Mass Air Flow) or VAF (Vane Air Flow) sensors. These sensors measure the amount of air entering the engine and the PCM/ECM uses this information in calculating the proper air/fuel mixture. Air entering the throttle body other than through the MAF or VAF sensor will not be accounted for in these calculations, causing a lean condition.

A lean condition can also be caused by a vacuum leak. When inspecting the air induction system, check vacuum lines, throttle body mounting and intake manifold sealing areas for vacuum leaks. Vacuum leaks can be found using propane. The engine will run smoother and there will be an engine rpm change when propane is discharged near a vacuum leak.

EXHAUST SYSTEM

Exhaust system components can fail due to physical or chemical damage. Since it is located under the vehicle, the exhaust system is subject to damage and wear from dirt, stones, water and other road hazards. The components in the system can also

rot out from the inside. When the engine is started from cold, combustion gases mix with condensation that forms when the hot exhaust contacts the colder exhaust parts, forming acids that corrode the metal. This type of failure is common on vehicles that are driven short distances, since the exhaust system never gets warm enough to evaporate the moisture.

Whether it is caused by physical or chemical damage, the result is cracks, holes or other damage to the exhaust system that cause excessive noise and can allow harmful exhaust gases to enter the passenger compartment. Engine exhaust contains CO, which can cause headache, nausea and drowsiness, and if enough is ingested, can even result in unconsciousness and death. Any exhaust system damage that results in exhaust leakage must be repaired immediately.

Damage to the exhaust system can also result in a restriction in the system. A blockage can be caused by physical damage, such as a dent in a pipe, or a clogged muffler or catalytic converter. A restriction can also be caused by a collapsed exhaust pipe. Some vehicles use double wall tubing for exhaust pipes. The inside tube can collapse or rust inside the outer tube and cause a restriction, even though the outer tube looks OK. Tap on the exhaust pipes with a mallet and listen for rattling or rust breaking loose, which would indicate a problem inside the pipe. A restricted exhaust system can cause a lack of power, poor fuel economy, backfiring, and if completely clogged, the engine may not run at all.

Begin exhaust system inspection by raising and safely supporting the vehicle. Visually inspect the exhaust system for physical damage, holes, cracks, separated components, bulging muffler seams, and broken or missing clamps and hangers. A catalytic converter that appears bluish or brownish indicates that it is overheating.

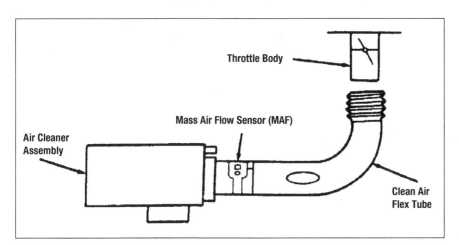

Typical air intake system. Makes sure there are no air leaks downstream from the MAF sensor or a lean condition could result.
(Courtesy: Ford Motor Co.)

Wiggle the exhaust system at various points to check for excessive movement caused by broken or cracked connections or broken or missing hangers. Tap on the exhaust system components with a mallet. A part that is in good condition will make a solid metallic sound, while a part that is worn out will have a dull sound. Rattling noises can be caused by loose heat shields, loose clamps or an exhaust pipe interfering with another component.

When tapping on the muffler, listen for the sound of loose rust particles. Mufflers usually rot out from the inside, so even if the outside of the muffler appears OK, it still may be ready for replacement.

A telltale sign of exhaust leakage is black streaks or soot on the outside of a component. However, if the source of exhaust leakage is not evident, you may have to start the engine and listen carefully for leaks at all joints. Do not overlook welded connections, as these can crack. A small exhaust leak will make a whistling, hissing or popping noise. A tapping sound that may sound like a valvetrain noise can actually be caused by an exhaust leak at the exhaust manifold/cylinder head juncture. Keeping in mind that the exhaust system will be very hot, carefully pass your hand close to a suspected leak area to see if escaping exhaust can be felt.

To check for a restricted exhaust system, connect a vacuum gauge to the intake manifold and start the engine. At idle, there should be approximately 17-21 in. Hg. vacuum. Accelerate the engine gradually to 2000 rpm. The vacuum should momentarily drop to zero and then return to normal without delay; if the exhaust is restricted, as the engine rpm is increased the vacuum will slowly drop to zero and slowly rise to normal. When closing the throttle, the vacuum should momentarily increase and then resume the normal reading; if the exhaust is restricted the vacuum will not increase when the throttle is closed. Accelerate the engine to 2500 rpm and hold. If the vacuum reading drops 3 in. Hg below the original reading after a few minutes, there is a restriction in the exhaust system.

A backpressure test can also be used to check for a restricted exhaust system. Remove the front oxygen sensor and install a suitable pressure gauge in the sensor hole. Start the engine and compare the pressure reading with specifications for the vehicle in question. A pressure reading that is higher than specifications indicates an exhaust restriction.

TURBOCHARGERS AND SUPERCHARGERS

In a normally-aspirated engine, when the piston moves down the cylinder on the intake stroke, a vacuum is created that draws the air into the cylinder. The air moves into the cylinder because the pressure in the cylinder is lower than the atmospheric pressure outside the engine. The more air that can be packed into the cylinders (along with a corresponding amount of fuel), the more power an engine will make, however, cylinder filling is limited in this type of engine because it is restricted to the amount of air that can be pushed by atmospheric pressure alone. This is why normally-aspirated engines are also known as atmospheric engines.

A supercharger or turbocharger is an air pump that forces air into the combustion chamber. In effect, a supercharger or turbocharger raises the pressure inside the intake manifold, so that when the intake valves open, more air (along with fuel on a gasoline engine) flows into the cylinders, resulting in an increase in power.

Superchargers are driven off the engine's crankshaft by a belt or gears, so some of the increased power that the supercharger generates is used to drive the supercharger itself. Turbochargers are driven by the engine's exhaust, so the power increase is said to be 'free' horsepower, since the turbocharger does not use any of the horsepower it creates.

Turbochargers

A turbocharger is divided into two sections, the turbine and the com-

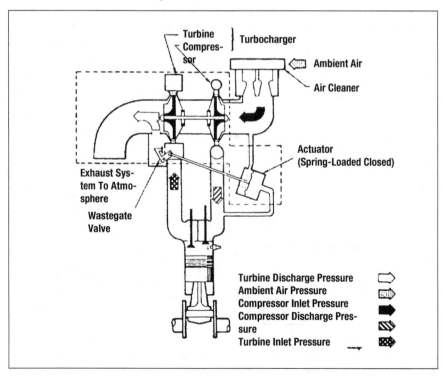

Turbocharger operation. *(Courtesy: GM Corp.)*

pressor. The turbine is attached to the exhaust manifold, where a turbine wheel inside the turbine housing is driven by the exhaust gas pressure and heat energy. The turbine wheel is connected by a shaft to the compressor wheel inside the compressor housing. The spinning of the turbine wheel causes the compressor wheel to spin, drawing in air to the compressor housing where it is compressed and pumped through ducts into the intake manifold. As the speed of the turbine increases, so does the pressure output, or boost, of the compressor.

Boost pressure must be limited to prevent engine damage. Boost is controlled by a wastegate or by shutting off the fuel supply to the engine.

A wastegate is a valve activated either by a diaphragm or a boost control solenoid. Wastegates are either integral to the turbine housing or are remotely mounted in the exhaust system. If controlled by a diaphragm, when a preset boost limit is reached, the diaphragm moves a rod that opens the wastegate. If controlled by a boost control solenoid, which is operated by the PCM/ECM, the wastegate opens and closes in response to sensor inputs to the PCM/ECM. When the wastegate is opened, excess exhaust pressure is released from the turbine housing, directed to the exhaust system and expelled into the atmosphere.

The fuel supply to the engine can be shut off by the PCM/ECM in response to inputs regarding intake manifold pressure or engine speed. The MAP (Manifold Absolute Pressure) sensor sends a signal to the PCM/ECM when a specified intake manifold pressure is reached. The PCM/ECM then cuts the fuel supply to the engine, causing boost and engine speed to decrease. When intake manifold pressure falls below the

limit, fuel delivery resumes. When boost is controlled in response to engine speed, the PCM/ECM will cut the fuel supply when inputs are received that a specific engine speed has been reached. Fuel delivery resumes when engine speed drops below the limit.

Inspection

Turbocharger related engine performance problems are caused by too little boost pressure or by overboost. These problems can usually be traced to a malfunction in the boost control system however, other components should also be inspected before any are condemned. If there is a lack of power, check for a dirty air cleaner, loose or restricted intake ducting or restricted exhaust system. Also check for exhaust leaks; if exhaust can escape before it reaches the turbine wheel, less boost (and power) will be produced. Listen for unusual noises coming from the turbocharger that could be an indication that the rotating assembly is binding or dragging.

A wastegate actuator that is stuck can be the cause of too little boost and low power if it is stuck open, or overboost if it is stuck closed. Overboost can cause detonation and possible engine damage. A wastegate can stick or bind due to carbon buildup

or be inoperative due a leaking diaphragm or vacuum hose. Check for free movement of the actuator by hand if possible and check for obstructions that could prevent free movement or closure. Wastegate operation can be checked using air pressure and a pressure gauge. Consult the appropriate service manual for testing procedures and pressure specifications.

WARNING: Turbochargers operate at extremely high temperatures. Do not touch the turbocharger while the engine is operating. Allow the turbocharger to cool sufficiently after the engine has been turned off before performing testing or servicing procedures.

If a wastegate problem is suspected, always check the ignition timing, knock sensor and vacuum lines before replacing the wastegate. If the wastegate is controlled by a boost control solenoid and the solenoid fails, a DTC should set in the PCM/ECM's memory and the MIL may illuminate.

Most turbocharger failures are caused by lubrication problems such as oil lag, restriction or lack of oil flow and foreign material in the oil. The exhaust flow past the turbine wheel creates extremely high temperatures, which creates a harsh operating environment for the turbocharger shaft bearings. Some manufacturers connect coolant lines to the turbocharger to cool the shaft bearings, but others rely on engine oil to lubricate and to cool. With the latter design, it is a good idea to let the engine idle for about a minute before shutting it off, particularly if the vehicle has been run hard, to let oil cool the turbocharger. If the engine is shut off immediately,

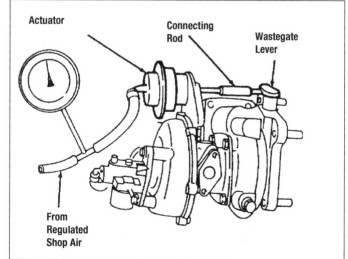

Testing wastegate operation using air pressure. *(Courtesy: Ford Motor Co.)*

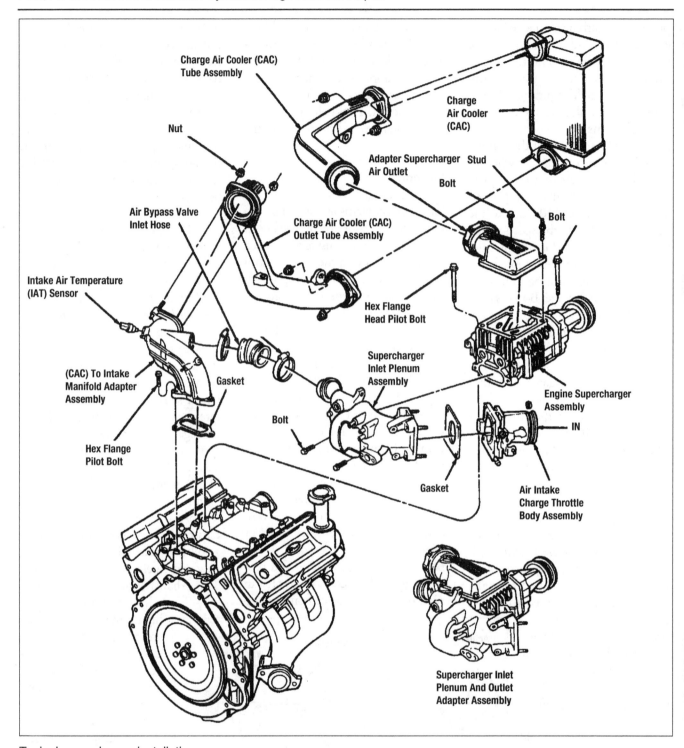

Typical supercharger installation.

the oil may burn causing hard carbon particles to form, which in turn will destroy the bearings.

When replacing a turbocharger, use new gaskets and torque all fasteners to specification. The unit should be preoiled prior to installation and the engine should not be revved before proper oil pressure has been established.

To prolong turbocharger service life, the oil and filter should be changed at regular intervals and the air filter should be inspected regularly. Inspect the routing and integrity of the oil supply and oil drain lines and check for oil leaks.

Superchargers

The amount of boost pressure a supercharger generates is determined by the size of the pulleys or gears on the crankshaft and supercharger, and by engine speed. The size of the pulleys or gears can be varied in order to get the desired boost. It may be necessary to drive the supercharger at a speed faster or slower than crankshaft speed. If the supercharger turns the same speed as the engine it is driven 1:1. If it's geared to turn faster for more or quicker boost, it is overdriven. If it's set up to run slower than the engine, it is under driven.

Otherwise, boost increases as engine speed increases.

To prevent supercharger cavitation, reduced performance and increased temperatures, a bypass valve is installed at the supercharger outlet. This bypass valve allows a controlled amount of air flow from the supercharger outlet back into the supercharger.

Proper supercharger performance depends on there being no vacuum leaks, which could cause a lean operating condition. Vacuum leaks can be detected using a propane cylinder as described in the Air Induction section.

Notes

Emissions Control Systems Diagnosis And Repair

POSITIVE CRANKCASE VENTILATION

Description And Operation

During engine operation, some combustion gases leak past the piston rings into the crankcase. These gases are commonly known as 'blowby'. The PCV (Positive Crankcase Ventilation) system vents crankcase gases into the engine air intake where they are burned with the air/fuel mixture.

The PCV system keeps pollutants from being released into the atmosphere, and also helps to keep the engine oil clean by ridding the crankcase of moisture and corrosive fumes. It also keeps crankcase pressure from building up and causing oil leaks as the pressure forces its way past seals and gaskets.

The PCV system is basically a controlled air leak from the crankcase into the intake manifold. Fresh air enters the crankcase through the breather cap or the ventilation filter inside the air cleaner. Atmospheric pressure pushes crankcase blow-by vapors toward the low-pressure point offered by the PCV valve and the intake manifold.

Inspection, Diagnosis And Testing

Inspect all PCV system hoses for cracks or other damage. Check the crankcase inlet air filter and replace as necessary.

Inspect the engine air cleaner. If the air cleaner is oil soaked and there is oil in the air cleaner, it may because the PCV valve or hoses are clogged. If the PCV valve and hoses are OK and these conditions are found, then the engine may be worn to the point it creates more blowby than the PCV

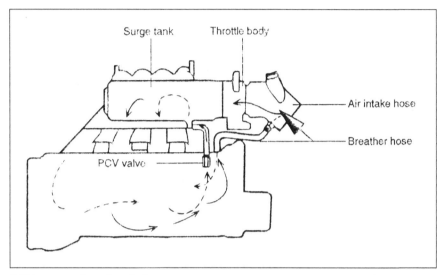

PCV system functional diagram   *(Courtesy: Hyundai Motor Co.)*

system can handle.

Start the engine and let it idle. Being careful not to damage the hose, use a suitable tool to pinch the hose between the intake manifold and the PCV valve. If the PCV valve is OK it should make a clicking sound when the hose is pinched and released.

Disconnect the PCV valve from its mounting grommet and listen at the valve. It will make a hissing noise if it is not clogged. Place your finger over the valve to check for vacuum. If there is little or no vacuum, check for a clogged or restricted hose.

Turn off the engine, remove the PCV valve from the engine and shake it. Listen or feel for the rattle of the valve plunger within the valve body. If it rattles the valve is not stuck

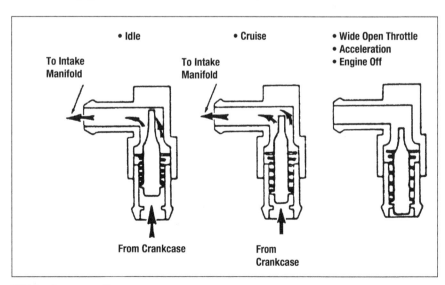

PCV valve operation.

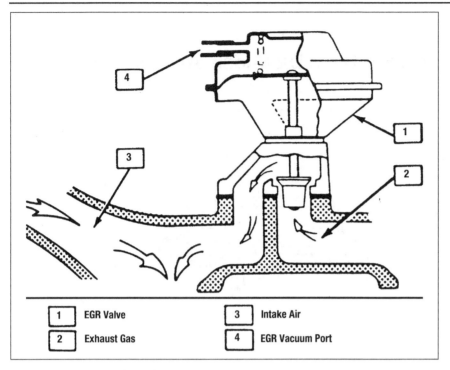

| 1 | EGR Valve | 3 | Intake Air |
| 2 | Exhaust Gas | 4 | EGR Vacuum Port |

Vacuum operated EGR valve

open or closed. If it doesn't rattle, the valve must be replaced.

Make sure the PCV valve is replaced with the correct one for the application. The spring inside the valve is calibrated for a specific flow rate. If the wrong valve is used, the engine can draw in excessive air, possible causing a high idle speed on vehicles with speed density fuel injection systems.

EXHAUST GAS RECIRCULATION

Description And Operation

Most of the air around us is made up of harmless nitrogen. Ordinarily, nitrogen cannot combine with oxygen. However, under very high heat conditions, such as those that occur inside an engine's combustion chamber, where temperatures can exceed 2500°F (1371°C), nitrogen molecules can bond with oxygen molecules and form oxides of nitrogen (NOx). When NOx leaves the tailpipe and is struck by sunlight, photochemical smog is formed.

A simple way to reduce NOx

would be to lower the temperature of combustion. This could be accomplished by running rich air/fuel mixtures, which contain a high level of cool liquid gasoline, or also by lowering thermostat temperatures. Unfortunately, both methods would produce high levels of HC and CO emissions and lower fuel economy, and are contradictory to the objective of using the minimum amount of fuel necessary for combustion. Burning leaner mixtures produces high temperatures.

The solution is to introduce a metered amount of an inert gas into the intake air stream. The gas takes up space that would otherwise be occupied by the regular incoming air/fuel charge, which contains 21% oxygen. Oxygen would contribute to combustion, and subsequently raise temperature. Replacing the oxygen with inert gas slows and cools the combustion burn.

Fortunately, a running engine produces large quantities of a suitable inert gas for this purpose: exhaust. Exhaust gas should theoretically contain very little, if any, oxygen because

it should have all been consumed during the combustion process.

The Exhaust Gas Recirculation (EGR) valve is used to meter the exhaust into the intake air stream. Most EGR valves consist of a vacuum operated diaphragm that is connected by a rod to a valve in its base, however on some EGR valves, control of the valve is fully electronic. The valve is located inside a connecting passage between the exhaust system and the intake manifold. When the valve opens, exhaust gas mixes with the incoming air that is to be used for combustion.

EGR function must be controlled because exhaust gas recirculation is not constantly required. EGR is not required when the engine is cold, at idle (warm or cold) and at WOT (Wide Open Throttle). Until the engine is warm, there is no need for exhaust gas recirculation because combustion is still sufficiently cool. Even when the engine is warm, there is no need for exhaust gas recirculation at idle because combustion pressures are relatively low and NOx is not formed, and exhaust gas recirculation would stall the engine because of too much dilution. At WOT, the need for power outweighs the need to control NOx emissions, and since WOT needs richer, and therefore slightly cooler mixtures, NOx formation is minimal anyway.

There are several systems currently used to control EGR function including ported, positive backpressure, negative backpressure, pulse-width modulated and electronic.

On the positive backpressure EGR valve, a control valve located in the EGR valve acts as a vacuum regulator valve. The control valve manages the amount of vacuum to the EGR diaphragm chamber by bleeding vacuum to atmosphere during certain operating conditions. When the control valve receives a backpressure signal from the exhaust through the hollow shaft of the EGR valve pintle,

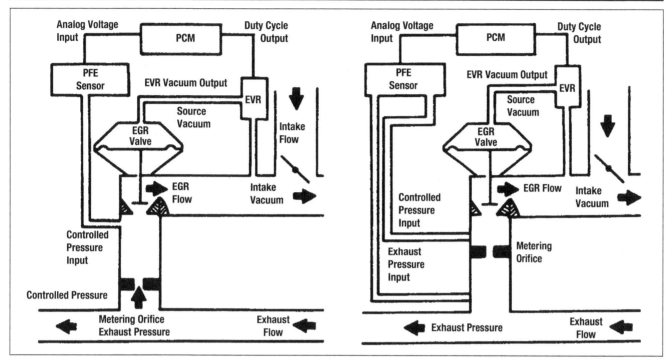

Typical Pressure Feedback EGR (PFE) system.
(Courtesy: Ford Motor Co.)

Differential Pressure Feedback EGR (DPFE) system.
(Courtesy: Ford Motor Co.)

pressure on the bottom of the control valve closes it. When the EGR valve closes, the full vacuum signal is applied directly to the EGR valve diaphragm, which opens the valve and allows exhaust gas recirculation.

On the negative backpressure EGR valve, a vacuum signal is supplied through a hose connected to the upper part of the EGR valve. Manifold vacuum is also applied to the lower diaphragm through an intake port at the base of the EGR valve. When manifold vacuum in the lower chamber isn't strong enough to overcome the spring tension on the lower diaphragm, a bleed valve closes allowing vacuum in the upper chamber to open the EGR valve. Exhaust flow opens a check valve in the pintle so that vacuum bleeds to atmosphere and the valve rises, but tries to drop again. This process controls EGR flow.

The pulse-width modulated EGR system is controlled entirely by the PCM/ECM. The computer controls the flow rate by sending electrical signals to a solenoid vacuum valve

between the PCM/ECM and EGR valve. The solenoid pulses up to 32 times per second. To determine pulse width, the PCM/ECM relies on a ported vacuum signal.

On computer controlled EGR systems, the PCM/ECM controls the vacuum signal to the EGR valve through a solenoid valve. The PCM/ECM uses coolant temperature, throttle position and MAP (Manifold Absolute Pressure) signals and sometimes other inputs, to determine solenoid operation. Whenever the engine is cold or idling, the solenoid valve blocks vacuum to the EGR valve. When the engine is warm and RPM is higher than idle speed, the solenoid ground is broken and vacuum opens the EGR valve.

Some systems, such as Ford Pressure Feedback EGR (PFE) and Differential Pressure Feedback EGR (DPFE) use a sensor in the exhaust stream that tells the PCM/ECM how much exhaust gas is actually flowing. With PFE, the PCM/ECM uses internal formulas to estimate the EGR flow. With DPFE, the PCM/ECM

actually gets a report on the flow by measuring the pressure above and below the EGR valve. The PCM/ECM then adjusts the EGR Vacuum Regulator (EVR) to optimize the EGR flow under various conditions.

The digital EGR valve allows the precise amount of EGR flow without using manifold vacuum. The valve controls EGR flow through three different size orifices for seven different combinations of EGR flow. When the PCM/ECM energizes a solenoid, the swivel pintle is lifted to open the orifice.

Some engines have an electronically controlled EGR valve. It has a control solenoid and EGR Valve Position (EVP) sensor. The return voltage signal ranges from 0.3 volts when it is closed up to 5 volts when it is fully open. The PCM/ECM controls EGR flow by pulsing the signal to the EGR solenoid. This provides better regulation of EGR flow than with conventional vacuum controlled EGR valves.

Diagnosis And Testing

When EGR function is not controlled properly, there is either not enough EGR when it is required, or there is too much EGR or EGR at the wrong time. When there is not enough EGR, driveability problems such as spark knock or surging at cruise can occur, as well as an increase in NOx emissions that could cause a failed emissions inspection. Symptoms of too much EGR or EGR at the wrong time include poor idle, stalling, hesitation, stumble and rough running during warm up, tip-in hesitation or stumble, surge at cruise, poor acceleration, and low engine vacuum.

Before blaming EGR function for any of these symptoms, be sure to check the basics as other components and systems could also be the cause. For example, carbon buildup in the combustion chamber could be the cause for that spark knock, and vacuum leaks could be the cause of hard starting and hesitation. Check EGR related scan tool data and check for DTCs that could narrow your troubleshooting focus.

Basically, the EGR system can malfunction in four ways: problems with EGR passages, problems with the EGR valve itself, problems with the vacuum control system and problems with the computer control system.

If you lift up on the EGR valve diaphragm (after protecting your fingers with a glove or shop towel) with the engine idling and there is no effect on idle speed, the EGR passages are probably clogged with carbon. Check the NOx readings using a five-gas exhaust analyzer. Run the engine until it reaches normal operating temperature and then increase engine speed to 2000 rpm. If the EGR system is functioning properly, the NOx readings should generally be below 1000 ppm (parts per million). If the NOx reading is above 1000 ppm and the EGR valve is functioning, then the EGR passages are probably clogged.

Remove the valve and clean the EGR passages until they are clear. Carbon stuck between the pintle and seat can also cause the EGR valve to not fully close causing poor idle, stalling or stumble after cold start.

Also keep in mind that if the EGR passages are only partially clogged, enough exhaust gas can enter the combustion chamber to make the engine run rough or stall at idle, but there still may not be enough EGR flow to control NOx emissions.

Conventional ported EGR valves can be tested simply using a hand operated vacuum pump. When vacuum is applied, the EGR valve should lift and maintain vacuum.

In order to test a positive backpressure EGR valve, a restriction in the exhaust system must be created to simulate exhaust backpressure. Place a suitable object in the tailpipe to restrict exhaust flow, then connect a hand operated vacuum pump to the EGR valve and apply vacuum. The vacuum should hold providing the diaphragm is not leaking. Start the engine and place the transmission in gear. The engine should stall when the restriction created exhaust backpressure builds up enough to open the EGR valve at idle.

To test a negative backpressure EGR valve, disconnect the vacuum hose from the EGR valve and connect a hand operated vacuum pump. With the engine off, apply vacuum and feel for diaphragm movement with your finger. The diaphragm should move up and hold vacuum. Have an assistant operate the ignition key. When the engine is cranked, you should feel the diaphragm drop, closing the valve.

Note that damage to the exhaust

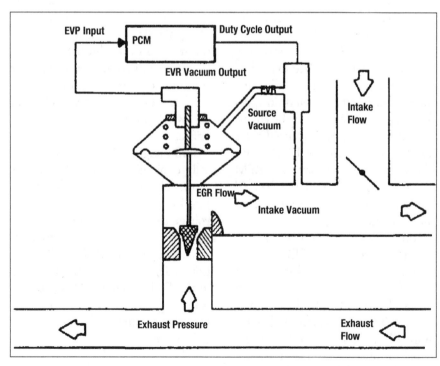

Electronically controlled EGR system. *(Courtesy: Ford Motor Co.)*

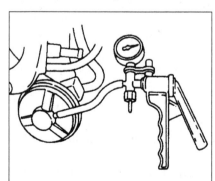

Testing an EGR valve with a vacuum pump. *(Courtesy: Ford Motor Co.)*

system that restricts exhaust flow (dented or collapsed pipe, clogged catalytic converter) or modifications which improve exhaust flow (aftermarket performance exhaust system) will affect the operation of a back-pressure EGR valve.

In order to function properly, vacuum operated EGR valves must receive the proper vacuum signal. Check for vacuum leaks caused by loose, broken, pinched or missing vacuum hoses. Check the hose routing against the schematic shown on the emissions label. Most systems use a TVS (Thermal Vacuum Switch) to prevent EGR when the engine is cold. If the switch is operating properly, it should not allow vacuum flow until the engine reaches a specific operating temperature.

Computer controlled EGR systems usually have a vacuum control solenoid controlled by the PCM/ECM. To test operation, use a tee fitting to connect a vacuum gauge into the hose at the EGR valve. With the engine warm, place the transmission in gear, apply the brakes and accelerate the engine. There should be a vacuum reading on the gauge. When the electrical connector at the solenoid is disconnected, vacuum should vent off and the gauge reading should be zero.

Some GM systems use a solenoid with a vent filter that can cause driveability problems if the filter becomes restricted, which could trap vacuum and hold the EGR valve open. Test these solenoids by covering the solenoid vent with your finger. The engine should stumble or stall. If it doesn't, the vent solenoid is probably defective.

Some Chrysler and import computer controlled systems use a back-pressure transducer. These systems are also tested in the same way as a positive backpressure EGR valve, using an exhaust flow restriction. Restrict the exhaust flow at the tailpipe, start the engine and unplug the solenoid. The engine should stall.

EGR System Service

One of the most common problems with EGR systems is the buildup of combustion deposits on the valve and in the manifold passages. Even when all components of the EGR system are operating properly, the engine may exhibit faulty EGR symptoms or in some cases even set a DTC if the manifold passages are blocked or restricted. Any time that the EGR valve is removed, the manifold passages should be inspected and cleaned with a wire brush or scraper.

SECONDARY AIR INJECTION (AIR)

Description And Operation

The Air Injection Reactor (AIR) system forces fresh air into the exhaust system to reduce HC and CO emissions. The oxygen in the fresh air combines with the post-combustion HC and CO to provide secondary oxidation, converting the residual HC and CO to water vapor and CO_2. The fresh air is fed into the exhaust stream at the cylinder head exhaust ports or in the exhaust manifold just past the exhaust ports, and on some vehicles, the catalytic converter. There are two kinds of systems: pump systems, that use an engine driven or electric pump to pump air into the exhaust system, and pulse-air systems, that use the natural pulses in the exhaust system to pull air into the exhaust system.

A basic pump air injection system consists of a belt driven air pump, a diverter valve to vent pumped air to atmosphere during engine acceleration to prevent backfire, a one-way check valve to allow air flow into the exhaust manifold or cylinder head and keep exhaust out of the air pump, and hoses and tubing to route the air to the exhaust manifolds or cylinder heads. Systems that include

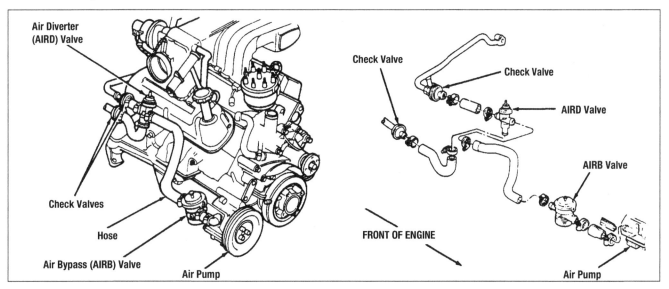

Typical air pump AIR system. *(Courtesy: Ford Motor Co.)*

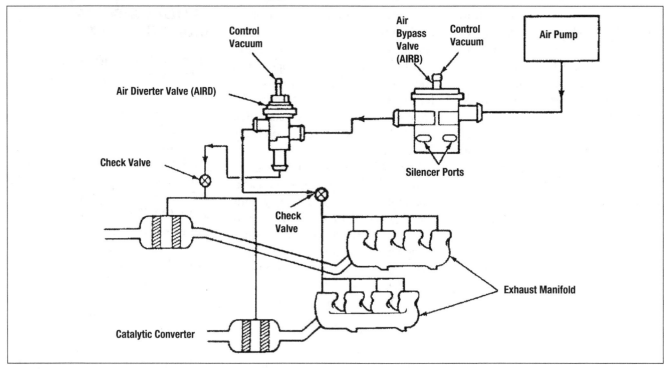

Diagram of a typical AIR system. *(Courtesy: Ford Motor Co.)*

the catalytic converter use an Air Bypass (AIRB) valve to direct pumped air to atmosphere or to an Air Diverter (AIRD) valve that directs air to the exhaust manifolds/cylinder heads or catalytic converter.

Intake air enters the pump through a centrifugal filter positioned behind the drive pulley. The filter consists of small fins that deflect airborne contaminants away from the pump as it rotates. Under certain conditions, pump air is delivered to the exhaust manifold(s), and on some vehicles, the catalytic converter. Check valves are used to prevent hot exhaust gases from backing up into the pump. When air is being supplied to the exhaust manifold for example, the check valve opens under pump pressure. When pump air is directed away from that location, exhaust system backpressure forces the check valve closed.

The AIRB and AIRD valves contain solenoids that are controlled by the PCM/ECM. These solenoids are used to direct air flow to a specific location depending on engine op-

erating conditions. Typically, air is directed to the exhaust manifolds/cylinder heads during open loop, when the engine is warming up. At this time, the rich air/fuel mixture that is used for engine start-up results in high amounts of unburned HC and CO in the exhaust. The oxygen in the incoming air combines with the HC and CO and oxidation continues.

The air is then switched to the catalytic converter when the engine has reached normal operating temperature and gone into closed loop. The air that is injected into the converter helps with the oxidation of HC and CO.

Under certain conditions, such as heavy acceleration, the addition of oxygen to the exhaust could cause a backfire. To prevent this, pump air is bypassed to the air cleaner or a remote silencer by the AIRB valve during this time.

Pulse-air systems use a reed valve, which responds to pressure pulses in the exhaust system. When an exhaust valve opens, a low-pressure area is created in the line extending from

the reed valve to the exhaust system. This causes the valve to open. Under this condition, air flows from the air cleaner through the open reed valve and into the exhaust, where it oxidizes unburned fuel and CO. When the exhaust valve closes, exhaust backpressure forces the reed valve closed.

Diagnosis And Testing

A faulty secondary air system can cause several problems including backfiring, excessive HC and CO emissions, and improper fuel control. The latter occurs when pump air is delivered to the exhaust manifold(s) during closed loop. This is because the oxygen sensor interprets the additional air as a lean condition. In response, the computer commands a rich mixture. Eventually, this condition will lead to poor fuel economy, rotten egg odor, an overheated converter, and/or an illuminated MIL. Always check for secondary air system related scan tool data and DTCs.

A functional check of the AIR system can be performed using a four- or five-gas analyzer. Run the engine

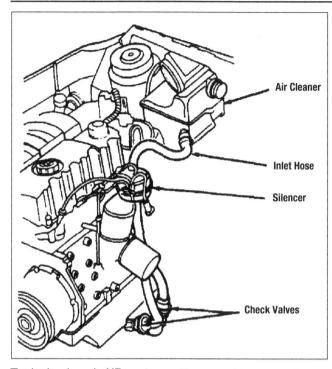

Typical pulse-air AIR system. *(Courtesy: Ford Motor Co.)*

at idle and record the exhaust gas readings. Then disable the AIR system by removing the pump drive belt or pinching off the hose to the air distribution manifold. Run the engine at idle and again record the exhaust gas readings.

When the engine was run without the AIR system, there should have been 2-5% less oxygen in the exhaust and the HC and CO readings should have increased. This would mean that the AIR system was injecting air into the exhaust system and thereby functioning properly. If there was no change in the readings with and without the AIR system, then the AIR system is not functioning properly. Check the system for the cause of the malfunction.

On pump driven systems, check the vacuum hoses and wiring in the system. Check the vacuum hoses for cuts, cracks and kinks that could cause a vacuum leak or a vacuum restriction. Also check hoses for flexibility; even though a hose appears OK, it could be hardened and ready to break. Use a vacuum diagram, such as that found on the vehicle

emissions control information label, to make sure all vacuum hoses are routed correctly. Carefully inspect the wiring for damage and corrosion.

Check the hoses, tubing and connections in the system for looseness, cracks, corrosion or other damage. Make sure the hoses and tubing are properly routed and connections are secure. Inspect the condition of the air pump drive belt and make sure it is properly tensioned.

If any hoses in the system show signs of burning, inspect the check valves for leaks. Disconnect the valve's input hose and, with the engine running at fast idle, hold your hand near the valve inlet. Replace the check valve if you feel exhaust gas leaking out. The valve can also be checked for leaks with an exhaust gas analyzer. With the engine running, hold the analyzer probe near the check valve opening. If any ex-

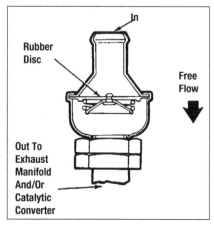

Cutaway view of an air check valve. *(Courtesy: Ford Motor Co.)*

haust gas is detected, then the valve is leaking.

If the system passes a visual inspection, check the air pump output. Start the engine and remove the outlet hose from the pump. Air should be coming from the pump outlet. A low pressure gauge can be used to measure the pump pressure. A properly functioning pump should typically produce 1-3 psi, but always check the manufacturer's specifications for the vehicle in question. If pressure is low, check the air filter for clogging before condemning the pump.

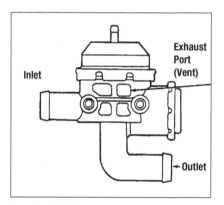

Typical AIRB valve. *(Courtesy: Ford Motor Co.)*

Start the engine and remove the vacuum hose from the Air Bypass (AIRB) valve. There should be a vacuum signal with the engine running. Reinstall the vacuum line and remove the outlet hose from the AIRB valve. Air should be coming from the hose. Reinstall the hose and open and quickly release the throttle. There should be a sudden release of air from the AIRB valve vent if there is air supply from the pump and the valve is working properly.

While the engine is warming up from a cold start, remove the hose from the Air Diverter (AIRD) valve that goes to the cylinder head or exhaust manifold. Air should be coming from the hose. If not, check for a vacuum signal at the vacuum hose to the valve. If there is an adequate vacuum signal (refer to the manu-

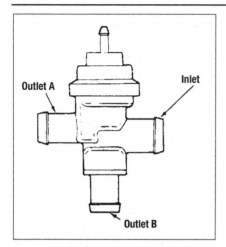

Typical AIRD valve
(Courtesy: Ford Motor Co.)

facturer's specifications) replace the AIRD valve. If there is no vacuum signal, check the vacuum hoses and the AIRD solenoid and wiring.

Once the engine reaches normal operating temperature, remove the hose from the AIRD valve that runs to the catalytic converter. When the engine is in closed loop, at normal operating temperature, air should be coming from the hose. If not, remove the vacuum line from the AIRD valve and check for a vacuum signal at the line. If there is no vacuum signal, replace the AIRD valve. If there is some vacuum (measured with a vacuum gauge), check the AIRD solenoid and wiring.

On pulse-air systems, visually inspect the hoses, tubes and valves of the system for damage and replace parts as necessary. Disconnect the hoses from the check valve inlet(s) and check the inside of the hoses for damage from hot exhaust gases. Replace the hoses and check valve(s), if damage is found.

Leave the inlet hose(s) disconnected and start the engine. Listen and feel for exhaust at the check valve(s). Intake air pulses should be found and the check valve(s) will make a burbling sound as air is drawn in. If exhaust is heard and/or felt, replace the valve(s).

CATALYTIC CONVERTER

Description And Operation

The catalytic converter contains a ceramic component coated with a catalyst. A catalyst is something that causes a chemical reaction without being part of the reaction. The catalyst agent is coated on a ceramic honeycomb structure or on small ceramic beads. A converter that uses the honeycomb structure is called a monolithic catalytic converter, while the kind that uses ceramic beads is known as a pellet catalytic converter. As exhaust flows through the converter, the catalyst agent causes a chemical reaction to take place, converting harmful exhaust gases to harmless ones.

The elements platinum, palladium and rhodium are used as catalysts in the catalytic converter. When HC and CO gases are exposed to hot surfaces inside the converter that are coated with platinum and palladium, the HC and CO combine with oxygen to become Carbon Dioxide (CO_2) and water (H_2O). Because platinum and palladium are called oxidizing catalysts, a catalytic converter that only reduces HC and CO is known as an oxidation converter, or two-way catalytic converter.

Three-way catalytic converters also contain the catalyst rhodium, which reduces NOx emissions. When NOx is exposed to a hot surface coated with rhodium, the oxygen is removed and only Nitrogen (N) remains. Because rhodium is called a reducing catalyst, a three-way catalytic converter is also called a reduction type converter. In a three-way converter, the oxidizing catalysts and reduction catalyst are separated in two compartments.

Most vehicles that are manufactured today also have a small catalytic converter that is part of the exhaust manifold or located just behind it. These converters are used to clean the exhaust during engine warm-up and are known as warm-up converters.

Most catalytic converters have fresh air injected into the converter by the

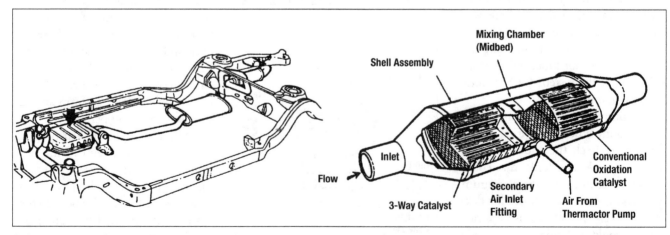

A three-way catalytic converter contains a reduction catalyst and an oxidizing catalyst. The reduction catalyst treats the incoming exhaust by reducing NOx into oxygen and nitrogen. The oxidation catalyst, with additional air from the AIR system, oxidizes HC and CO into CO_2 and water.

AIR system. The extra air helps in the oxidation of HC and CO. The PCM/ECM controls when the air is injected. If air is injected at the wrong time the converter could overheat or actually produce more NOx.

A catalytic converter can fail in several ways. If the engine is run with leaded gas, the catalysts in the converter can become coated with lead, making them useless. Leaded gas is no longer generally available, so this type of failure is rare.

The converter can become clogged if exposed to an overly rich air/fuel mixture, which can overheat the converter and melt the ceramic substrate.

The catalytic converter can also fail like any other exhaust system component, due to rust or physical damage. Over time, the ceramic substrate can come loose in the converter and slowly disintegrate, which is indicated by a rattling noise when the converter is struck with a mallet.

Diagnosis And Testing

A catalytic converter must be replaced if it leaks, if it is clogged or if it does not function properly. Check for catalytic converter related scan tool data and DTCs.

If exhaust leakage is suspected, visually inspect the converter for holes, cracks or other physical damage. A telltale sign of exhaust leakage is black streaks or soot on the outside of the converter. However, if the source of exhaust leakage is not evident, you may have to start the engine and listen carefully for leaks. A small exhaust leak will make a hissing or popping noise.

While inspecting the converter, tap on it with a mallet. If the converter makes a rattling sound, it means that the ceramic substrate has come loose and is disintegrating, and the converter must be replaced.

The catalytic converter can become clogged from using leaded gas or if exposed to an overly rich air/fuel mixture, which can overheat the con-

verter and melt the ceramic substrate. A clogged converter can cause a lack of power, poor fuel economy, backfiring, and if completely clogged, the engine may not run at all.

To determine if the converter is clogged, perform the vacuum test or backpressure test described in the exhaust system inspection section of this study guide. To isolate the source of the restriction, disconnect the exhaust system one part at a time, until the vacuum or pressure readings are normal.

If a converter is being replaced because it is clogged, the cause of the clog must be determined and repaired or the replacement converter will also clog. A cylinder that is misfiring due to an ignition problem (bad plug wire, etc.) or mechanical problem (valve not seating, etc.) will allow raw fuel to enter the exhaust system, and also may cause the PCM/ECM to enrich the mixture in the other cylinders because it detects the unused oxygen from the dead cylinder. This can cause serious overheating in the catalytic converter, which can melt the ceramic substrate, clogging the converter.

A simple test for whether a catalytic converter is functioning properly is by measuring the inlet and outlet temperatures. With the engine at normal operating temperature, check the temperature of the exhaust inlet and outlet surface before and after the converter using a temperature probe and a DMM or an exhaust pyrometer. The exhaust surface temperature should be at least 100°F (38°C) hotter than the intake surface temperature. If not, the converter is probably not operating at peak efficiency. Since the converter needs oxygen to convert HC and CO into CO_2 and water, this may be caused by a problem in the AIR system.

WARNING: Be very careful when performing this test as catalytic conversters operate at extremely

high temperatures.

Another test can be performed using a four- or five-gas exhaust analyzer. For proper results with this test, there should be no defects in the vehicle's ignition, fuel or O2 feedback systems, no leaks in the exhaust system, and the analyzer must be calibrated and working 100% properly.

Disable the air injection system, if equipped, since any extra air in the exhaust will produce unreliable results. Bring the engine to normal operating temperature and make sure it enters closed loop. Connect the analyzer to the exhaust system.

Run the engine at 2000 rpm and note the exhaust readings. If the converter is cold, the readings should continue to drop until the converter reaches full operating temperature.

When the readings stabilize, check the oxygen level; it should be close to zero, indicating that the converter is using all available oxygen. There is one exception to this however. If there is no CO left for the converter to use, there may be a little oxygen in the exhaust. If there is too much oxygen and no CO in the exhaust, stop the test and verify that the system is in control. If not, perform the necessary repairs and retest.

If the system was in control, use a propane enrichment tool to bring the CO level up to about 0.5%. The oxygen level should drop to zero, because the converter now has enough CO to convert.

Once a solid oxygen reading is being obtained, snap the throttle wide open and let it drop back to idle. Check the rise in oxygen level; it should not rise past 1.5%.

If the converter passes the above tests, it is working properly. If the converter fails the tests, its efficiency is probably compromised, if it is functioning at all.

OBD II systems use an oxygen sensor mounted downstream from the catalytic converter to check converter efficiency. This sensor checks the oxygen content of the exhaust after it leaves the converter and is known as a catalyst monitor. If the signal from the catalyst monitor is too similar to the signal from the primary oxygen sensor, it means that the converter is not functioning properly.

EVAPORATIVE EMISSIONS CONTROLS

Description And Operation

The purpose of the evaporative emissions control system (EVAP) is to prevent HC emissions from escaping the fuel system to atmosphere. Prior to the introduction of EVAP systems, fuel vaporized and was emitted to the atmosphere from vented gas caps and carburetor float bowls, polluting the environment. The EVAP system is designed to capture these vapors and route them to the

engine where they become part of the air/fuel mixture and are burned during combustion.

All EVAP systems contain a pressure/vacuum relief fuel cap, vapor valve, charcoal canister, canister purge valve and the necessary plumbing connecting the fuel tank and the canister, and the canister and the engine intake.

The fuel tank cap contains a pressure and vacuum relief valve. The vacuum valve acts to allow air into the fuel tank to replace the fuel as it is used, while preventing fuel vapors from escaping the tank. The vapor valve is located on or near the fuel tank and allows fuel vapor but not liquid fuel to flow from the tank to the charcoal canister.

The charcoal canister contains activated charcoal that adsorbs the fuel vapors from the fuel tank. When

something is adsorbed, it is held on the surface like a magnet, as opposed to being absorbed, which is akin to being sucked up, like with a sponge. The canister stores the fuel vapors when the engine is not running. When the engine is running, under certain operating conditions, a valve between the canister and engine opens, fresh air is drawn in through the canister air filter and the air and fuel vapors are drawn into the engine and burned, 'purging' the canister.

Where EVAP systems differ is in when and how canister purging takes place. Early systems used ported vacuum and a check valve to make sure purging would not occur at idle and thermovalves to make sure purging only occurred after the engine reached a certain operating temperature. As emissions requirements became more stringent, more sophis-

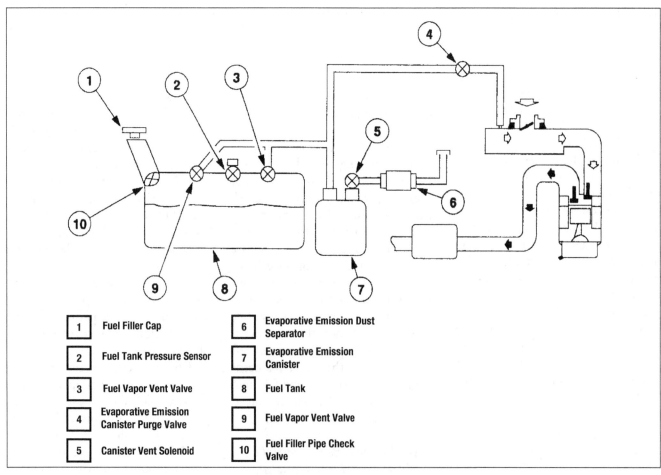

1 Fuel Filler Cap	**6** Evaporative Emission Dust Separator
2 Fuel Tank Pressure Sensor	**7** Evaporative Emission Canister
3 Fuel Vapor Vent Valve	**8** Fuel Tank
4 Evaporative Emission Canister Purge Valve	**9** Fuel Vapor Vent Valve
5 Canister Vent Solenoid	**10** Fuel Filler Pipe Check Valve

Typical evaporative emissions control system *(Courtesy: Ford Motor Co.)*

ticated purging controls were called for. Today charcoal canister purging is controlled by the PCM/ECM. The PCM/ECM determines when the canister should be purged based on various sensor inputs. When purging is needed, the PCM/ECM operates a solenoid valve, which controls the vacuum to purge the canister. Generally, the purge solenoid is activated when the engine is running above idle speed and at normal operating temperature.

OBD II vehicles have enhanced EVAP systems (leak detection). A fuel tank pressure sensor and canister vent solenoid are added to the EVAP system for diagnostic purposes. The solenoid is located in the fresh air supply hose to the sealed charcoal canister. On a non-enhanced EVAP system, the canister is open to the atmosphere. The canister vent solenoid is normally open, allowing fresh air to be drawn into the canister. The PCM/ECM activates the solenoid during the EVAP leak test to block the entrance of outside air.

Diagnosis And Testing

The EVAP system can malfunction and allow fuel vapors to escape into the atmosphere or cause driveability problems like rough idle and stalling. Begin diagnostics by checking for any EVAP related scan tool data and DTCs.

Visually inspect the system, looking for cracked, broken or missing vapor hoses, which can cause vacuum leaks and fuel odors. Make sure all hoses are routed properly and connections at the tank, canister and engine are secure. Check the electrical wiring and connections for looseness, corrosion and chafing.

Inspect the fuel cap and gas tank filler neck for damage and correct fit. On OBD II vehicles, a cap that is not installed securely may set a DTC.

Inspect the canister for cracks or other damage. Be sure to inspect the canister air filter to make sure it is not clogged. If fresh air cannot be drawn into the canister, the fuel vapors cannot be purged. The filter is replaceable on some canisters, but on others the entire canister must be replaced.

To check EVAP system function, connect a scan tool to the DLC. Start the engine and let it idle. Using the scan tool, determine whether the solenoid is on or off. At idle the purge solenoid should be off.

Leave the scan tool connected and drive the vehicle. When the engine operating conditions for purging are met, again check the scan tool for purge solenoid operation. The solenoid should be on. If the solenoid is not on, check the power supply to the solenoid and the solenoid itself.

Purge solenoid valves can be tested to see if they will pass or block vac-

uum using a remote source of voltage and a hand vacuum pump. However, you must first determine whether the solenoid is normally closed or normally open. A normally open solenoid permits vacuum flow when de-energized. A normally closed solenoid blocks vacuum until it is activated by the PCM/ECM.

Enhanced EVAP

To test system integrity, the PCM/ECM can close the canister vent solenoid and open the purge valve. This will cause the fuel tank pressure sensor to indicate a vacuum if the system is properly sealed. If the vacuum fails to reach a certain level during two consecutive tests under the same conditions, the MIL will be illuminated and one or more DTCs will be set. The cause could be a loose fuel cap, a vapor hose loose or damaged, or a stuck open canister vent solenoid.

The system can also test for small leaks by closing the canister vent solenoid and purge solenoid and waiting for a loss of vacuum. If the vacuum drops too quickly during two consecutive tests under similar conditions, a DTC will set.

Some vehicles with enhanced EVAP systems may be able to perform additional tests and may have additional components. Always consult the vehicle service manual for information.

Notes

Computerized Engine Controls Diagnosis And Repair

ENGINE CONTROL SYSTEM OPERATION

In order to provide a combination of good overall performance, good fuel economy, and low emissions, computerized engine control systems became necessary. Simpler mechanical controls can no longer do the job alone.

Earlier automotive computers controlled only a single function, such as ignition timing or air/fuel mixture. Today's computers, commonly known as PCMs (Power-train Control Modules) or ECMs (Engine Control Modules), control air/fuel mixture, ignition timing and other functions.

All engine control systems have the same basic format of inputs, the PCM/ECM and outputs, which communicate using electronic circuits. Information is gathered by a wide variety of sensors, using several means. Some sensors vary a resistance to ground for temperature or pressure sensing. Some sensors report movement by a variable resistor. Other sensors vary a frequency output as pressure or air flow changes. All sensors supply the PCM/ECM with information on engine conditions.

Once the PCM/ECM sees what the operating conditions are, it compares what it sees to pre-programmed reference parameters in its ROM (Read Only Memory) or PROM (Programmable Read Only Memory), which it uses to adjust to changing engine conditions. Outputs are voltage commands, such as providing power or ground to circuits, or varying the pulse width of a square wave to control timing or injection.

Typical inputs are sensors such as the O2 (oxygen) sensor, ECT (Engine Coolant Temperature) sensor, MAP (Manifold Absolute Pressure) sensor, and TP (Throttle Position) sensor. On the output side of the computer, typical actuators include fuel injectors, an ignition timing module, an idle speed control motor, a cooling fan relay or an EGR control solenoid.

Most computerized engine control systems have self-diagnostic capabilities. When the ignition key is turned ON, the PCM/ECM sends out a 5-volt reference signal to its sensors and controlled devices, and examines the return signals from them as indications of the particular conditions to which they are being subjected. At the same time, the PCM/ECM is checking for problems within the system. It does this by comparing these inputs with its internal memory of what probable signals should be.

Suppose, for example, after the engine is running, the TP sensor indicates a closed throttle, the CKP (Crankshaft Position) sensor indicates 1000 RPM, but the MAP sensor registers atmospheric pressure instead of idle intake manifold pressure. By comparing these signals, the PCM/ECM recognizes an incompatibility. It knows that this is an impossible combination of signals, so it stores the information about this problem in its memory.

Problems that are found by the PCM/ECM during self-testing are stored as either hard faults or intermittent failures. Each type is assigned a number that represents a DTC that is stored in the PCM/ECM's memory. A hard fault is a problem that is found in the system at the time of the self-test, while an intermittent problem is a malfunction that occurred in the past, but is not present at the time of the self-test. Intermittent faults are usually stored for a specific number of key ON/OFF cycles, and are then erased from the PCM/ECM's memory if they do not reappear during that period.

Most of the time, when a DTC is stored in memory, the PCM/ECM will illuminate the MIL (Malfunction Indicator Light) (also known as the CHECK ENGINE or SERVICE ENGINE SOON light) to show that service is needed. Under normal conditions, the MIL will come on for a few seconds when the ignition key is turned ON and during engine cranking, but should go off when the engine starts. If the MIL comes back on, it means that there is probably a DTC stored in memory.

ENGINE CONTROL SYSTEM DIAGNOSIS AND TESTING

Diagnosis of electronic engine control systems should be performed in a logical manner. This begins with not automatically assuming that the problem is with the engine control system! Make sure the basic engine and related conventional systems are sound, using inspections and tests like those described elsewhere in this study guide, before getting involved with testing sensors. A driveability problem can be caused by something as simple as a broken vacuum line.

Become familiar with the capabilities of the engine control system on the vehicle you are servicing, using available service literature. Check TSBs (Technical Service Bulletins) for information about problems and fixes discovered in the field and not covered in the service manual.

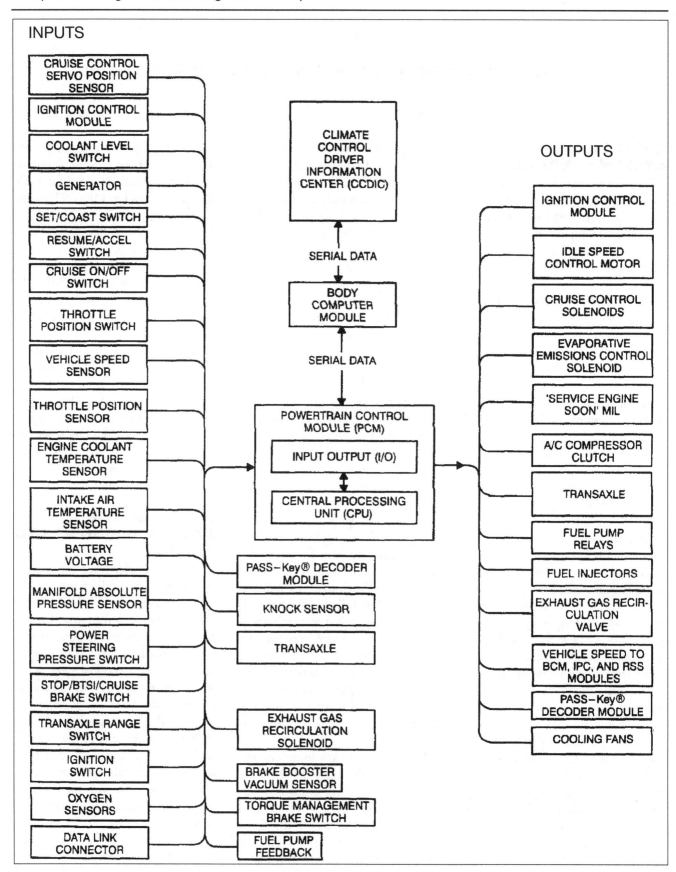

Inputs and outputs in a typical electronic engine control system.   *(Courtesy: GM Corp.)*

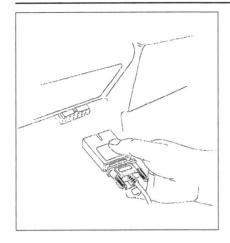

The DLC (Data Link Connector) on all OBD II vehicles is located under the dash on the driver's side of the vehicle. *(Courtesy: Snap-on Tools)*

If the MIL is illuminated or you suspect that there are DTCs stored in the PCM/ECM memory, the codes can be retrieved in several ways. On some older vehicles, a jumper wire can be connected between terminals of the DLC, which causes the engine control system to go into self-diagnostic mode. The MIL then flashes and codes can be read by interpreting the flashes with a service manual. On other vehicles, the codes can be read on a digital display on the instrument panel.

A scan tool must be used to obtain codes from OBD II systems, but it is also a better choice for older vehicles as well since a scan tool can perform tests and read datastream values. The scan tool may require an adapter to connect to the DLC on older pre OBD II vehicles, and it must be loaded with the proper data cartridge for the year, make and model of the vehicle being serviced.

Once all codes are retrieved and recorded, determine whether they are hard faults or intermittent faults. Clear the PCM/ECM memory following the manufacturer's recommended procedure. On OBD II vehicles codes can be cleared using a scan tool, while on some older vehicles the battery may have to be disconnected. Drive the vehicle and watch for the MIL to illuminate. Any codes that reappear are hard faults and should be serviced first.

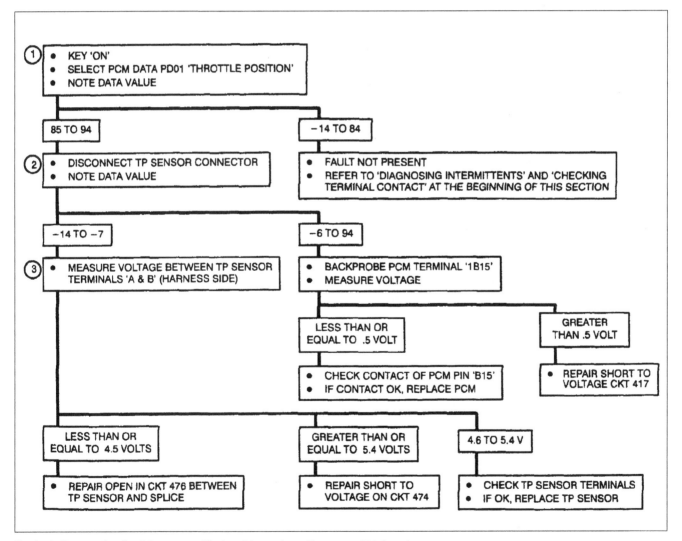

Typical diagnostic chart for a specific trouble code. *(Courtesy: GM Corp.)*

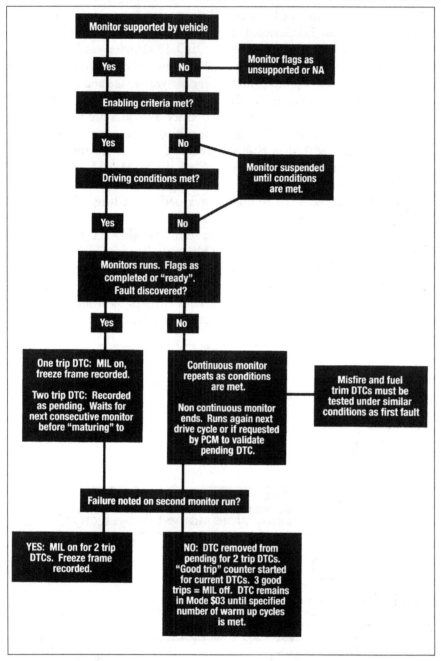

OBD II monitor flowchart.

ing. These values can then be compared with the manufacturer's specifications. Since a value that is not within spec should in theory set a DTC, a value that is almost out of spec might not set a DTC but could indicate a problem area.

Intermittent driveability problems are usually more difficult to diagnose and repair. You may have to try to recreate conditions described by the driver to get an intermittent code to reset. Since intermittent problems are often caused by damaged wiring and connectors, tapping and wiggling wiring harnesses and connectors can also get problems to reoccur and reset codes.

A scan tool feature that is helpful for finding intermittent problems is the ability to take a 'snapshot' of the engine control system operating parameters. A vehicle with an intermittent problem can then be driven in an attempt to recreate the conditions for the problem. When the symptoms appear, the technician can then record the system electrical values. The technician can then analyze the data to see what values changed at the time of the malfunction.

OBD II Monitors

The PCM/ECM on OBD II vehicles performs continuous tests on emissions-related systems and components. These tests are known as 'monitors'. Some monitors run all the time and are called 'continuous' monitors. Others are run once per drive cycle and are referred to as 'non-continuous' monitors.

A drive cycle consists of a set of conditions necessary to run the monitor to completion. This usually involves operating the vehicle while in closed loop under specific operating conditions. Always refer to the vehicle shop manual, as each monitor has a specific 'enable criteria'—the conditions that must be met for a monitor to be completed—and the criteria varies among models and manufacturers.

Once you have the DTCs that require diagnosis, refer to the appropriate service information to identify the systems and circuits that the DTCs represent. The diagnostic charts will describe the circuit and the fault that the code represents and contain troubleshooting procedures and tests that must be performed, to determine the cause of the malfunction. These tests usually describe various voltage and resistance measurements using a DMM.

If the vehicle exhibits driveability problems like rough idle, stalling, surging or hesitation, but does not set any codes, refer to the symptom-driven diagnostic charts contained in most manufacturer's service manuals.

Scan tool datastream values can also be invaluable when there are no codes. Datastream values are the actual electrical values of the engine control system sensors and actuators measured while the engine is operat-

There are three kinds of tests that can be performed during a monitor. The first is where the PCM/ECM tests a component's electrical circuit for opens and shorts to power or ground. The second involves comparing data between sensors to see if the information makes sense (as in our earlier CKP/MAP sensor example). In the last type of test, the PCM/ECM can check the function of output devices by commanding the component and checking the result.

If the monitor results indicate a failure, a fault will be recorded in the PCM/ECM's memory. For some faults, the PCM/ECM will set a DTC and turn on the MIL. However, for most DTCs the PCM/ECM must see the same fault occur during two 'trips'. A trip is a completed drive cycle. After the first trip, the fault is recorded as 'pending'. Once the PCM/ECM sees the same fault the next time the monitor runs, the PCM will turn on the MIL. If the same fault is not seen during the next monitor, the pending code will be cleared.

If the MIL is turned on because of a particular DTC, and the monitor responsible for that DTC runs three times in a row without seeing the failure, the PCM/ECM will then turn off the MIL. However, the DTC will remain in the PCM/ECM's memory until a certain number of warm-up cycles occur.

To check monitor status, connect a scan tool to the DLC. On some scan tools you may have to access Mode $01. 'Complete' or 'ready' indicate monitors that have run successfully. 'NA' or 'not available' indicates monitors that are not used on this particular vehicle. Monitors shown as 'not ready' or 'incomplete' means that either the drive cycle criteria have not been met and the monitor isn't finished or a related monitor has recorded a fault.

Just because a monitor has not completed does not mean that it cannot be useful in achieving a diagnosis. Examine the vehicle service information to see how the system operates. Look for information on conditions that are necessary for a monitor to complete. Here you may find that a fault derived from one monitor is keeping others from completing. Also look for what various incomplete monitors have in common. Access Mode $07 and look for pending faults that may indicate an impending failure. Being able to look at the engine operating conditions at the time a code was set can also assist with diagnosis. This 'freeze frame data' can be accessed in Mode $02.

Once repairs are completed, use Mode $04 on the scan tool to clear codes and reset all monitors. Operate the vehicle in a manner necessary to satisfy the drive cycle requirements for the monitor that set the DTC in question. Recheck the monitor status and check for pending codes to see if the fault returned.

Service Precautions

The following precautions should be observed when testing or servicing components and circuits of an electronic engine controls system:

- Never disconnect any electrical connector with the ignition switch ON. This creates high voltage spikes, known as short duration transients, which can permanently ruin delicate circuits
- Some electronic engine control circuits are designed to carry very small amounts of current. For this reason, a high-impedance (over 10 megohms) digital meter must always be used when troubleshooting computer-related circuits
- Always connect the negative lead of a voltmeter first.
- Never use a test light unless specifically instructed to do so in the manufacturer's diagnostic procedure

- To prevent damage from electrostatic discharge, always touch a known good ground before handling an electronic component. This is especially important after sliding across a seat or walking a distance
- Do not touch the terminals of an electronic component unless it is necessary, as oil from skin can cause corrosion.

Electrical Testing

In order to perform diagnostic tests, a technician must be able to measure voltage, voltage drop, amperage and resistance using a DMM.

Voltage Measurements

If there is a DC/AC switch, make sure it is switched to the DC position. Set the function/ range control to the desired volts position. If the magnitude of the voltage is not known, set the switch to a range that will read the most voltages seen on the vehicle. (Normally, a 20V range will be sufficient). Reduce the range until you have a satisfactory reading. Connect the test leads to the circuit being measured and read the voltage on the display.

Resistance Measurements

Set the function/range control to the desired position. If the magnitude of the resistance is not known, set the switch to the highest range, then reduce until a satisfactory reading is obtained. If the resistance being measured is connected to a circuit, turn off the power to the circuit being tested. Turn off the ignition. Connect the test leads to the circuit being measured and read the resistance on the display.

Voltage Drop

Each component in a circuit has some resistance value, and the voltage is reduced as it moves the circuit's resistive loads. The sum of all the voltage drops across a circuit will equal

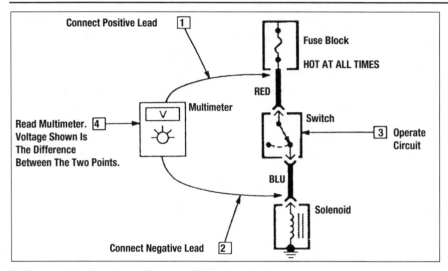

Using a voltmeter to perform a voltage drop test.

the original amount of applied voltage. Voltage never disappears—it is merely converted into another form of energy by the resistance of the load or wires.

The voltage available at any point depends on the circuit resistance. The higher the resistance, the more voltage is needed to force current through the circuit. Resistance of any type will use some voltage potential, so the use of voltage is lost across any type of resistance.

To measure voltage drop, set the voltmeter switch to the 20-volt position. Connect the voltmeter negative lead to the ground side of the resistance or load to be measured. Connect the positive lead to the positive side of the resistance or load to be measured. Read the voltage drop directly on the 20-volt scale.

A high voltage reading is a sign of too much resistance. Converse-ly, if the voltage drop is too low, then that condition signifies too little resistance.

Amperage Measurements

An ammeter is connected in series with the circuit, so all the current passing through passes through the ammeter. This means that the fuse must be removed from the circuit, or a connection broken. The ammeter is then inserted into the circuit to replace the fuse or join the two halves

of the circuit, observing proper polarity with an analog meter.

Connect the ammeter as you would a voltmeter, with the red or positive probe connected on the battery positive side of the circuit, and the negative lead toward the ground side of the circuit or the battery negative terminal. When working on the voltage side of the load, the negative lead would then be on the load side of the ammeter. If working on the ground side, the positive lead would be on the load side of the ammeter, and the negative lead would then be on the side away from the load.

The ammeter should always be set to the highest range before starting to take a measurement. Then, lower the setting one notch at a time until a usable reading is obtained. If the reading is more than half the scale on an analog ammeter or more than half the digital range on a digital ammeter, don't switch to a lower range. This will protect an analog unit from damage. A digital unit will not be able to give a reading if the amperage measured is out of range.

Engine Control System Sensors

Oxygen Sensor

The oxygen sensor (O2S) is located in the exhaust stream, ahead of the

catalytic converter, on the exhaust manifold or exhaust pipe. It is used to detect the concentration of oxygen in the exhaust gas. Input from the oxygen sensor is used by the PCM/ECM to regulate the air/fuel mixture. Using highly refined metals (zircon and platinum), the sensor uses differences between the oxygen content of the surrounding air and the oxygen content of the exhaust to generate a voltage, which is transmitted to the PCM/ECM. The computer in turn reacts to the changing voltage value by adjusting the fuel metering at the fuel injectors.

There is an opening in the oxygen sensor that is exposed to atmosphere. The atmosphere contains 21% oxygen, so this percentage is used as a reference with which to compare the oxygen content of the exhaust. The oxygen sensor's voltage signal ranges from zero to one volt. Signals below 450 mV indicate a lean condition (excessive oxygen), while readings above 450 mV point to a rich condition (little residual oxygen).

Most newer vehicles use a heated oxygen sensor (HO2S), which contains a heating element that brings the sensor to operating temperature faster. Since an oxygen sensor must be hot (at least 500°F) in order to work, the heating element allows the PCM/ECM to use the sensor's input signals sooner. The heating element also stabilizes the temperature of the sensor during cold weather.

Several oxygen sensors may be installed on a vehicle. V6 and V8 engines can have a sensor installed in each manifold. The sensor(s) that is located closest to the engine is used to check the exhaust oxygen content as the exhaust leaves the engine and is known as a primary sensor. A secondary sensor may be installed closer to the catalytic converter to monitor the oxygen content of the exhaust before it enters the converter.

OBD II systems use a sensor mounted downstream from the cata-

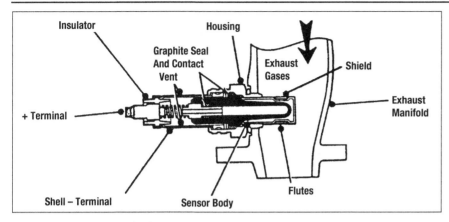

Cutaway view of a typical oxygen sensor.

lytic converter to check its efficiency. This sensor checks the oxygen content of the exhaust after it leaves the converter and is known as a catalyst monitor.

Since the oxygen sensor signal is used by the PCM/ECM to regulate the air/fuel mixture, a faulty oxygen sensor can cause the PCM/ECM to meter the fuel delivery incorrectly, causing overly rich or lean misfire conditions.

Inspect the oxygen sensor wiring for cuts and abrasion and contamination from oil or transmission fluid. The cavity in the sensor that senses the oxygen content in the atmosphere must be clear for the sensor to function properly. Disconnect the electrical connector and inspect the terminals for corrosion, distortion and contamination.

Start the engine and allow it to run until it reaches normal operating temperature. The oxygen sensor must be tested with the engine at normal operating temperature and the engine control system in closed loop.

Connect the positive lead of a DMM to the sensor signal wire and the negative lead to the engine ground. The voltage reading should fluctuate as the oxygen sensor detects varying levels of oxygen in the exhaust stream.

If the sensor reads above 550 mV constantly, the air/fuel mixture is probably too rich or the sensor may be contaminated from carbon caused

by rich air/fuel mixtures, the use of leaded fuel, or from silicones found in antifreeze or sealers. If the sensor voltage reads below 350 mV constantly, the air/fuel mixture may be too lean, there may be an exhaust leak near the sensor, diluting the reading, there may be high resistance in the wire between the sensor and the PCM/ECM, or the sensor may be defective.

Under normal conditions, the sensor should fluctuate high and low. If the sensor voltage does not fluctuate, the sensor may be defective. However, before condemning the sensor, try forcing the system rich by restricting the air intake or injecting propane into the air inlet. The voltage reading should increase to 800-900 mV. Then, force the system lean by pulling off a large vacuum hose. The voltage reading should drop to 200-300 mV.

If the voltage did not change accordingly when the system was forced rich or lean, then the sensor is defective and must be replaced. Remove the sensor from the exhaust system and examine its appearance. Black sooty deposits on the sensor tip may indicate a rich air/fuel mixture. White gritty deposits could be an internal antifreeze leak. Brown deposits indicate oil consumption. All of these contaminants will destroy a sensor, and if the problem is not repaired the new sensor will also be destroyed.

If the catalytic converter is func-

tioning properly, the voltage signal from the catalyst monitor will fluctuate very little in comparison to the signal from the primary oxygen sensor. If the signal from the catalyst monitor is too similar to the signal from the primary oxygen sensor, it means that the converter is not functioning properly.

Camshaft Position Sensor

The Camshaft Position (CMP) sensor determines when Top Dead Center (TDC) compression of the No. 1 cylinder occurs and then converts it into a pulse signal that is sent to the PCM/ECM. The PCM/ECM uses the signal to determine correct injection sequence. The sensor may be located in the distributor housing; it may obtain its signal from the camshaft timing gear; or, on vehicles with distributorless ignition systems, the CMP sensor may be in an assembly that replaces the distributor. Regardless of its location, in all cases this sensor reacts to the camshaft position.

Essentially, there are two types of camshaft sensors. One is a Hall effect switch and the other is a magnetic reluctance sensor, or PM generator (permanent magnet generator). The easiest way to distinguish the Hall effect switch from magnetic sensors is to remember that the Hall effect switch will have a three-wire harness and control an existing voltage and the reluctance sensors usually have two wires and create a voltage.

If there is spark at the coil or if the fuel injectors are injecting fuel, the problem is most likely not the cam sensor.

When suspecting a camshaft sensor problem, first perform a visual inspection; most problems can be found in wiring harnesses and connectors.

To test a Hall effect switch, set a DMM to the volts setting and check the voltage between the power and ground wires. This voltage may be 4, 6, 8 or 12 volts depending on the system. Take note of this voltage reading.

Connect the DMM between the signal terminal and the ground wire. Rotate the engine with the starter motor by tapping the ignition key. When the engine is rotated, the signal should fluctuate between 0 volts and the system voltage noted in the earlier step. While rotating the engine, check for damaged shutter blades or any indication that the shutter blades are hitting the magnet. You can use a scope to monitor the half wave pulses, which you should see on the output wire. If the hall switch is powered and grounded properly, and the mechanical parts move as intended when the engine is cranked, you should see the pulses. If not, the switch is bad.

To check a magnetic reluctance sensor, disconnect the sensor connector. Using a DMM set to the ohms setting, check resistance across the sensor terminals. The resistance should be approximately 500 to 1200 ohms at 70°F (21°C). Resistance will vary with temperature. This test should be performed with the ignition on and engine off. Using a thin piece of steel, check the tip of the sensor to be certain that it is magnetized.

Crankshaft Position Sensor

The Crankshaft Position (CKP) sensor generates a signal to the ignition module, which results in a reference pulse being sent to the PCM/ECM. The PCM/ECM uses this signal to calculate crankshaft position and engine speed for injector operation.

As with camshaft sensors, there are two types of crankshaft sensors. One is a Hall effect switch and the other is a magnetic reluctance sensor.

There is also a dual crankshaft or combination sensor. This design combines two sensors and is normally mounted on a pedestal on the front of the engine, near the harmonic balancer. This type of crankshaft sensor is usually a Hall effect switch, and usually requires adjustment during replacements. Failure to make this adjustment will usually allow the sensor to be struck by the rotating vanes behind the harmonic balancer, damaging both the vanes and the new sensor.

Magnetic reluctance type crankshaft sensors are usually mounted on the side of the engine, protruding into the block. You can test the voltage output of these permanent magnet sensors (PM generators) by measuring their voltage output, which varies by cranking rpm. Record some readings on known good sensors in use in vehicles you service, so you'll have benchmark values by which to judge the output of these sensors when a similar vehicle comes in with a no-start condition.

Testing of each type of crankshaft sensor is the same as testing of the camshaft sensor types.

Knock Sensor

The Knock Sensor (KS) is mounted in the engine block or manifold. When spark knock or pinging is present, the sensor produces a voltage signal that is sent to the PCM/ECM. The PCM/ECM will then retard the ignition timing based on these signals.

When suspecting a knock sensor problem, first perform a visual inspection. Most problems can be found in wiring harnesses and connectors. The voltage and resistance at the knock sensor can be checked using a DMM. Refer to the vehicle manufacturer's test procedures and specifications.

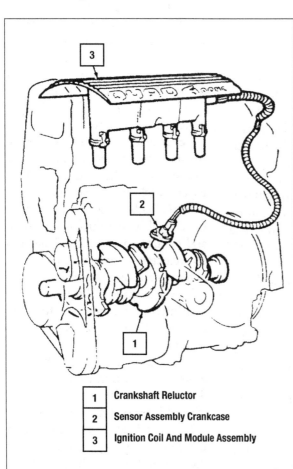

1	Crankshaft Reluctor
2	Sensor Assembly Crankcase
3	Ignition Coil And Module Assembly

Magnetic reluctance type crankshaft sensor
(Courtesy: GM Corp.)

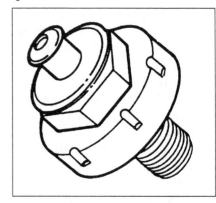

Typical knock sensor. It contains a piezoelectric crystal that produces an AC voltage under vibration

Intake Air Temperature Sensor

The Intake Air Temperature (IAT) sensor advises the PCM/ECM of changes in intake air temperature (and therefore air density). As intake air temperature varies, the PCM/ECM, by monitoring the voltage change, adjusts the amount of fuel injection according to the air temperature. These sensors, like the similar coolant temperature sensors, are 'negative coefficient' sensors, meaning that the resistance varies inversely by temperature. More voltage is dropped across the sensor when it is cold, and less when hot. This is why you see a low voltage reading (0.5 to 0.6v) across a coolant sensor at operating temperature.

If you don't want to use live voltage readings, unplug the electrical connector from the IAT sensor. Using an ohmmeter, measure the resistance between both terminals. The resistance should be approximately 3000 ohms at room temperature (70°F, or 21°C). The intake air temperature sensor and coolant temperature sensor resistance values are usually the same. Because of this, an easy test on a cold engine (sitting overnight) is to compare the resistance values of the two sensors. If the engine is cold, and both sensors are the same temperature, the resistance values should be about the same.

Start the engine, and as it warms up check that the values change

ECT And IAT Sensors		
Temperature vs. Resistance Values (approximate)		
°F	°C	ohms
210	100	185
160	70	450
100	38	1,800
70	20	3,400
40	4	7,500
20	–7	13,500
0	–18	25,000
–40	–40	100,700

Typical resistance values of a Negative Temperature Coefficient (NTC) sensor

smoothly, or heat the sensor up using a hair dryer to see if the values change smoothly.

If the resistance value doesn't change, the sensor is probably defective. A thermometer and a table of expected voltages are also an easy way to test the sensor at a wide range of temperatures. Some manufacturers build the intake air temperature sensor into the air flow sensor. In this case, they are usually replaced as a unit. Since this type of sensor is expensive, careful testing should be performed to make certain that it is defective.

Engine Coolant Temperature Sensor

The PCM/ECM sends the Engine Coolant Temperature (ECT) sensor a voltage and the sensor varies the voltage according to coolant temperature. When the sensor fails, it can prevent the system from going into closed loop. Depending upon its failure mode, it can also cause poor fuel economy and hesitation or stalling when the engine is cold. The ECT sensor is also a Negative Temperature Coefficient (NTC) sensor and is tested similar to the IAT sensor.

Manifold Absolute Pressure Sensor

The PCM/ECM sends the Manifold Absolute Pressure (MAP) sensor a voltage and the sensor varies the voltage according to manifold vacuum or engine load. A bad MAP sensor can cause poor fuel economy, poor driveability and detonation. There are two types of MAP sensors, the analog signal type, which

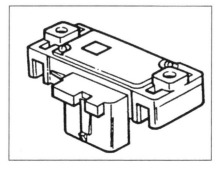

Manifold Absolute Pressure Sensor

is tested with a voltmeter, and the frequency signal type, which is tested with a hertz meter or digital tachometer. If you are not certain with which type the vehicle is equipped, check the reference voltage (usually around 5 volts), and then check the signal voltage. If the signal voltage never changes from 2.5 volts, it is most likely a frequency type. If still not certain with which type the vehicle is equipped, check the service manual.

Analog signal type sensors are usually located in the engine compartment near the air cleaner, mounted on the inner fender or firewall. They can be checked using a DMM and a hand vacuum pump. Disconnect the MAP sensor electrical connector. Connect one jumper wire from the connector to the MAP sensor's terminal A. Connect the other wire from the connector to terminal C.

Connect the positive lead of a DMM to terminal B and the negative voltmeter lead to ground. Turn the ignition key ON. If the reading falls in the range of 4.6 to 5.0 volts, the sensor is functioning properly, at this point. Start the engine and let it idle. An idling engine will produce a large amount of intake manifold vacuum, which should pull the MAP sensor's voltage down to a low reading of approximately 1 to 2 volts (reading will vary with altitude). This test indicates that the MAP sensor is responding to vacuum. Check the service manual for the specifications for the vehicle you are testing.

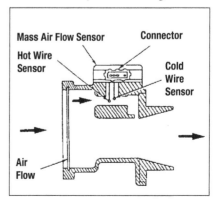

Cross section of a Mass Air Flow sensor

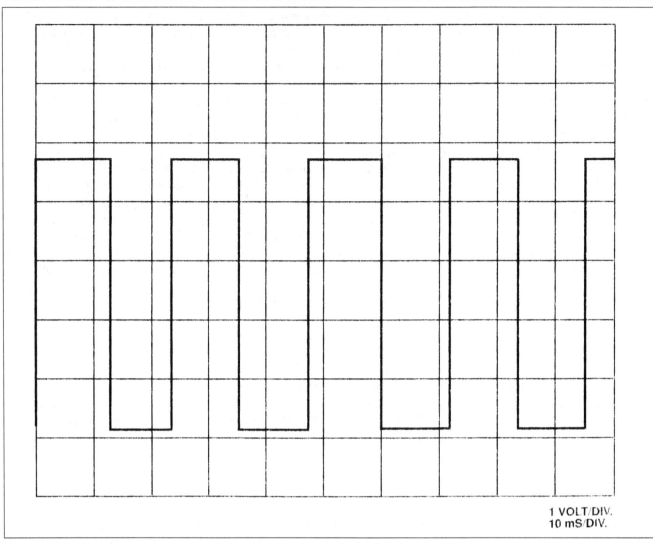

1 VOLT/DIV.
10 mS/DIV.

Typical MAF sensor signal on an oscilloscope. *(Courtesy: GM Corp.)*

MAP sensor frequency can be measured with a digital tachometer. Never use an analog tachometer. A tachometer is a frequency counter. It measures pulses received per second (Hz) and converts them to rpm. If in doubt, always refer to the vehicle service manual for values and testing procedures.

Mass Air Flow Sensor

In the Mass Air Flow (MAF) sensor, incoming air flow cools a heated wire inside the sensor. The temperature, and therefore the resistance, of the heated wire varies according to changes in air flow. The PCM/ECM monitors the amount of power required to keep the heated wire at a

specified temperature. The PCM/ECM uses this information to determine the operating conditions of the engine to control fuel delivery. A large quantity of air indicates acceleration, while small quantities indicate deceleration or idle. These values must correspond to the actual condition. In other words, if a large air flow is indicated, the throttle should be open and the rpm high.

You can test the MAF with a DMM or an oscilloscope. The waveform on an oscilloscope should appear as a series of square waves. The frequency should increase smoothly and proportionately when engine speed and intake air flow is increased. If the frequency is erratic, the MAF

or circuit wiring is defective.

Another method of checking a MAF sensor is to measure the pulse width of the fuel injector. Pulse width is a measurement of how long the fuel injector is open, or how much fuel the fuel injector is delivering. Restrict the air intake and look for a change in fuel control. If a change in fuel delivery is noticed, the MAF sensor is most likely working properly.

Some MAF sensors are sensitive to vibration. Gently tap on the MAF; if the engine idle changes, the MAF sensor is defective.

The symptoms of a bad MAF sensor include hesitation or stumbling during acceleration, stalling or intermittent stalling during acceleration,

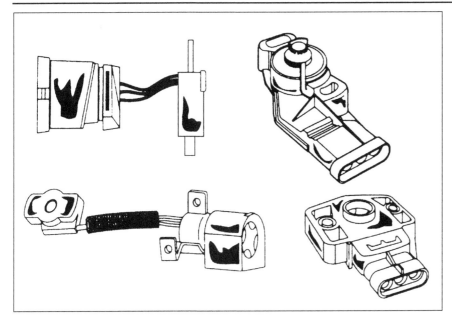

Various types of throttle position sensors

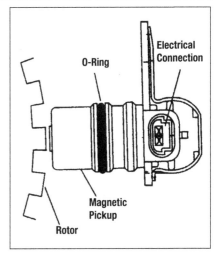

Diagram of a typical Vehicle Speed Sensor (VSS). *(Courtesy: GM Corp.)*

misfiring under load, and surging at cruising speeds.

Always be sure that the air duct from the air flow sensor to the throttle body or intake manifold is connected and in good condition. If the duct falls off or engine backfiring blows it off, the engine won't start. Furthermore, air leaks in the duct will lean out the fuel mixture and may cause lean-related performance problems. Remove the duct and inspect it closely to look for cracks in the rubber.

Throttle Position Sensor

Throttle Position (TP) sensors are usually located on the side of the fuel injection throttle body. These are most often variable resistors. TP sensors can be checked using a DMM set to the volts setting. TP sensor failure is common because it has parts that move each time the accelerator is depressed or released. This is one of the more common parts that require replacement or adjustment, due to the amount of movement this sensor endures every time a vehicle is driven. However, it is one of the easiest components to test and replace. Be certain the problem is the sensor, and not its connector.

Before testing a TP sensor, perform a visual inspection. To test most TP sensors, disconnect the TP connector and install jumper wires from the sensor connector to the wiring harness. You can attach test leads to the jumpers, or you can use 'bed of nails' test clips on the harness. This permits the sensor to operate properly during testing. Most TP sensors use three wires: a 5-volt reference wire, a signal wire to the PCM/ECM and a ground wire. Some may have additional wires, used for integral switches in the sensor.

Connect a DMM set to the volts setting between the signal wire (usually the center terminal) and the ground wire (one of the outside terminals) on the TP sensor. This test should be performed with the ignition ON and the engine OFF.

Check the voltage reading with the throttle in the idle position. Usual voltage readings are approximately 0.45 volts.

Open the throttle slowly. The voltage should increase smoothly as the throttle is moved to the WOT (Wide Open Throttle) position. Usual voltage at the WOT position is approximately 4.5 volts.

Release the throttle slowly. The

voltage should decrease smoothly as the throttle is moved to the idle position. Erratic readings or a momentary infinite reading indicate a defective sensor. The voltage test of a TP sensor is best accomplished using a scope, as even the smallest dropouts can be easily seen as the throttle is moved.

Vehicle Speed Sensor

The vehicle speed sensor is a permanent magnet sensor. The VSS consists of a permanent magnet surrounded by a coil of wire. A toothed ring, also called a reluctor, is located on the transmission's output shaft. The VSS and the reluctor are positioned so that a slight air gap (generally 0.050 in.) is maintained between the two. As the output shaft turns, the reluctor causes the magnetic field of the VSS to continually change from strong to weak. This produces an alternating current output, which increases in both frequency and amplitude as vehicle speed increases.

The VSS produces its own voltage. The resistance of the coil windings in the VSS is typically around 1200 ohms. Always check the manufacturer's specification when performing diagnosis. The computer uses the VSS signal to control shift timing, TCC (Torque Converter Clutch) application, cruise control and the electronic speedometer.

To test the VSS, disconnect the wiring connector from the sensor and connect the leads of a DMM, set on the ohms position, to the sensor terminals. Compare the resistance reading with the manufacturer's specifications. High or infinite resistance readings are caused by excessive resistance or possibly an open circuit. If the resistance reading is low there is a short circuit.

Next, change the DMM to the AC volts position. Raise and safely support the vehicle so the drive wheels are off the ground. Start the engine and place the gear selector in Drive. Observe the DMM as the engine speed is increased. The voltage reading should increase smoothly as engine speed increases.

The VSS can also be checked using a lab scope. In place of the DMM, connect the lab scope leads to the sensor terminals. When the speed is constant, a sine wave pattern should appear on the scope. As speed is increased the AC signal should change in amplitude and frequency.

PCM/ECM Reprogramming

Over the years, the OEMs (Original Equipment Manufac-turers) have found it necessary in many cases to reprogram vehicles' PCM/ECMs with changes to correct various performance problems. These changes are usually detailed in TSBs. On pre-OBD II vehicles, it was common practice to replace a PROM (Program-mable Read Only Memory) or chip to update the PCM/ECM. However, OBD II vehicles do not have replaceable PROMs. OBD II PCM/ECMs have an EEPROM (Electrically Erasable Program-mable Read Only Memory) chip, which can be reprogrammed without removing the unit from the vehicle.

At first, updates could only be installed using a manufacturer-specific tool, but because the U.S. EPA (Environmental Protection Agency) wants the aftermarket to be able to perform emissions-related repairs and they cannot require shops to purchase specific brands of tools, the SAE (Society of Automotive Engineers) and the tool and equipment industry developed communication protocol J2534. This is a translator that allows a PC (Personal Computer) to communicate with the PCM/ECM on all makes and models. The translation software is contained in a pass-through device that connects to the PC and the vehicle's DLC.

Before reprogramming a PCM/ECM, the existing calibration must be identified. This can be done using Mode $09 on a scan tool and then checking a calibration list at the OEM web site.

The updates and installation programs are available through the OEM web sites. To program a PCM/ECM without using a factory scan tool, you need the software, a PC or laptop computer running the Windows 2000 or later operating system, a high-speed Internet connection and the pass-through tool. A high-speed Internet connection is essential because the programs are large and would take many hours to download using a dial-up connection. It is also recommended that a stand-alone PC or laptop be used, instead of one that is also used for other jobs in the shop. Other computer processes can interrupt or stop the reprogramming process, which can ruin the PCM/ECM.

Two software packages are needed for programming, the updated PCM/ECM software and the computer program that installs the software on the PCM/ECM. These can usually be downloaded to the PC or

laptop before connecting the computer to the pass-through tool, however some manufacturers require a 'live' link between the vehicle and the OEM's server while the PCM/ECM is being updated.

As stated earlier, interrupting reprogramming can cause the process to fail and possibly ruin the PCM/ECM. To avoid this, pop-up blockers, virus protection and firewall software must be turned off. E-mail programs, screensavers and all other automatic processes should be disabled.

Another way that reprogramming can be interrupted is if the vehicle's battery voltage drops. During reprogramming, battery voltage to the PCM/ECM and the pass-through tool gets power from the OBD II connector and must remain constant. The ignition switch must be turned on for part of the process, which may automatically turn on lights or other loads that could cause a significant battery voltage drop. To avoid this, connect a second fully charged battery to the vehicle battery with jumper cables. Do not use a battery charger.

Reprogramming can also be interrupted if something is accidentally turned on, like the vehicle's interior lights. Before starting the job, make sure the key is in the ignition and the driver's window is down. Make sure the security system is turned off.

Once all safeguards against interruption are in place and the software is downloaded into the PC, start the reprogramming application and follow the process step-by-step. Once reprogramming is completed, the PCM/ECM will have to undergo a relearning procedure, which may be as simple as completing a drive cycle, but could also require more reprogramming. Information on relearning procedures is usually available at the OEM web sites.

Prepare yourself for ASE testing with these questions on
ENGINE PERFORMANCE

NOTE: The following questions are written in the ASE style. They are similar to the kinds of questions that you will see on the ASE test. However, none of these questions will actually appear on the test.

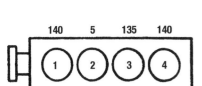

Compression Specs
140 psi

140   5   135   140

1. After the compression readings shown above were taken, a wet compression test was made. The second set of readings was almost the same as the first. Technician A says that a burned valve could cause these readings. Technician B says that a worn piston ring could cause these readings. Who is right?
   A. Technician A only
   B. Technician B only
   C. Both A and B
   D. Neither A or B

2. Blue smoke is coming from the exhaust pipe of a vehicle. Technician A says that worn piston rings could be the cause. Technician B says that a bad head gasket could be the cause. Who is right?
   A. Technician A only
   B. Technician B only
   C. Both A and B
   D. Neither A or B

3. A vacuum gauge is connected to the intake manifold of an engine and the engine is run at 2000 rpm. During the test, the pointer on the gauge fluctuates rapidly between readings of 10 and 22 inches of vacuum. These test results point to:
   A. a leaking intake manifold gasket.
   B. worn piston rings.
   C. worn valve guides.
   D. a weak or broken valve spring.

4. Engine detonation (knock) could be caused by any of the following EXCEPT:
   A. a lean air/fuel mixture
   B. retarded ignition timing
   C. excess carbon in the combustion chambers
   D. a stuck-closed EGR valve

5. A vehicle with electronic ignition hesitates and stumbles during acceleration. The problem goes away when the vacuum advance hose is disconnected and plugged. Technician A says that a stuck vacuum advance mechanism could be the cause. Technician B says that an intermittent open in the pickup coil leads could be the cause. Who is right?
   A. Technician A only
   B. Technician B only
   C. Both A and B
   D. Neither A or B

6. Technician A says that spark advance on an engine can be tested by listening to the way the engine sounds at higher rpm. Technician B says that spark advance on an engine can be tested with a timing light that incorporates an ignition advance meter. Who is right?
   A. Technician A only
   B. Technician B only
   C. Both A and B
   D. Neither A or B

7. A regular customer presents his vehicle for service. He describes symptoms of poor driveability and says that the vehicle has been repaired for the same problem in the past. Which, of the following, should you do first?
   A. connect the vehicle to an engine analyzer
   B. check for diagnostic trouble codes
   C. check the vehicle service history and check for TSBs, service campaigns and recalls
   D. perform a cylinder balance test

8. Two technicians are listening to a tapping noise coming from the top end of a V8 engine. Technician A says the noise could be a valve needing adjustment. Technician B says the noise could be an exhaust leak. Who is right?
   A. Technician A only
   B. Technician B only
   C. Both A and B
   D. Neither A or B

STANDARD®

Professional automotive training.

On-Site and On-Demand.

Prepare yourself for ASE testing with these questions on
ENGINE PERFORMANCE

9. Technician A says a high spike line on an oscilloscope indicates a disconnected or open plug wire. Technician B says a high spike line indicates a closed gap on a spark plug. Who is right?
   - A. Technician A only
   - B. Technician B only
   - C. Both A and B
   - D. Neither A or B

10. A vehicle can be started with great difficulty, but lacks power, and will not idle. Technician A says that there could be a hole or tear in the duct between the mass air flow sensor and the throttle body. Technician B says that a restricted fuel filter is the problem. Who is right?
   - A. Technician A only
   - B. Technician B only
   - C. Both A and B
   - D. Neither A or B

11. A vehicle is towed in with a 'cranks but won't start' condition. A 'noid' light test finds no injector pulses, and Technician A says the vehicle needs a computer. Technician B finds no spark, and says the vehicle needs an ignition module. Who is right?
   - A. Technician A only
   - B. Technician B only
   - C. Both A and B
   - D. Neither A or B

12. Technician A says that evidence of cylinder wear can be found using a cylinder leakage tester. Technician B says that a blown head gasket can be found using a cylinder leakage tester. Who is right?
   - A. Technician A only
   - B. Technician B only
   - C. Both A and B
   - D. Neither A or B

13. A poor running vehicle has low fuel volume. Technician A tests the electrical connector at the tank, and finding system voltage available, says the vehicle needs a new pump. Technician B says high circuit resistance may prevent the pump from operating properly. Who is right?
   - A. Technician A only
   - B. Technician B only
   - C. Both A and B
   - D. Neither A or B

14. An engine with an electronic fuel injection system has high fuel pressure at idle. This could be caused by a:
   - A. low manifold vacuum.
   - B. leaking fuel pump check valve.
   - C. plugged fuel injection valve.
   - D. high manifold vacuum.

15. With the engine off, vacuum is applied to a positive backpressure EGR valve using a hand held vacuum pump. Technician A says that the EGR valve should open. Technician B says that the valve will not open unless a restriction is created in the exhaust and the engine is started. Who is right?
   - A. Technician A only
   - B. Technician B only
   - C. Both A and B
   - D. Neither A or B

16. Technician A says that valves should be adjusted when the piston is at TDC on the compression stroke and both valves are closed. Technician B says that hydraulic lifters should be adjusted to zero lash. Who is right?
   - A. Technician A only
   - B. Technician B only
   - C. Both A and B
   - D. Neither A or B

17. While the engine is running, a technician pulls the PCV valve out of the valve opening and places his finger over the valve. No vacuum is felt. Technician A says that the PCV valve could be stuck closed. Technician B says that the hose between the intake manifold and the PCV valve could be plugged. Who is right?
   - A. Technician A only
   - B. Technician B only
   - C. Both A and B
   - D. Neither A or B

18. The wiring diagram symbol shown above is for a:
   - A. resistor
   - B. variable resistor
   - C. transistor
   - D. thermistor

19. A vehicle gets poor fuel mileage and has poor heater performance. Which of the following could be the cause?
    A. a bad ECT sensor
    B. a defective fan clutch
    C. a clogged cooling system
    D. a stuck open thermostat

20. A vehicle with electronic fuel injection gets poor gas mileage. Engine tests show a rich mixture. Technician A says that a bad O_2 sensor could be the cause. Technician B says that a bad IAT sensor could be the cause. Who is right?
    A. Technician A only
    B. Technician B only
    C. Both A and B
    D. Neither A or B

21. With a DMM connected, the O_2 sensor reads above 550 millivolts constantly, Technician A says that the fuel mixture is probably too rich. Technician B says the fuel mixture may be too lean or there may be an exhaust leak near the sensor. Who is right?
    A. Technician A only
    B. Technician B only
    C. Both A and B
    D. Neither A or B

22. There are two types of MAP sensors: the analog signal type, which is tested with a voltmeter, and the frequency signal type, which is tested with a Hertz meter or digital tachometer. To determine which type the technician has, he performs a reference voltage and signal voltage check. The signal voltage doesn't changes from 2.5 volts. It is most likely:
    A. a frequency type
    B. an analog type
    C. could be either type
    D. none of the above

23. A vehicle has sluggish performance and high fuel consumption. Testing reveals that the vehicle fails to enter closed loop operation. Technician A says the ECT sensor may be defective. Technician B says the TP sensor may be set incorrectly. Who is right?
    A. Technician A only
    B. Technician B only
    C. Both A and B
    D. Neither A or B

24. A vehicle is towed in for a no start condition. Spark tests good, and an examination of the throttle body shows fuel pouring from the TBI injector when the engine is cranked. Technician A says the fuel injector is stuck open. Technician B says the PCM driver for the injector is shorted out. Who is right?
    A. Technician A only
    B. Technician B only
    C. Both A and B
    D. Neither A or B

25. A turbocharged vehicle performs poorly and lacks power. All of the following could be the cause EXCEPT:
    A. restricted intake duct
    B. a wastegate that is stuck open
    C. failed turbocharger shaft bearings
    D. a wastegate that is stuck closed

26. An oxygen sensor voltage is being monitored on a scope type analyzer. A pattern is observed to change from 0.25 volts to 0.8 volts in a regular, series of flat-topped 'hills'. Technician A says that this is normal, closed loop operation. Technician B says that this indicates intermittent operation, and the sensor needs replacement. Who is right?
    A. Technician A only
    B. Technician B only
    C. Both A and B
    D. Neither A or B

27. When troubleshooting a slow drain on the battery, which diagnostic tool should be used?
    A. ohmmeter
    B. ammeter
    C. voltmeter
    D. test light

28. While testing a starting circuit on a V8 engine, the technician finds that the engine cranks slowly, the starter current draw is 90 amps, and the battery voltage while cranking is 11 volts. What should the technician do next?
    A. check the voltage drop of the starter motor circuit
    B. test the battery capacity
    C. replace the starter motor, as a short is indicated
    D. determine the condition of the engine

Prepare yourself for ASE testing with these questions on
ENGINE PERFORMANCE

29. A V6 engine with distributorless ignition breaks up on acceleration, but gets smoother when reaching cruise. Technician A says a bad coil pack is the problem. Technician B says the cam sensor must be replaced. Who is right?
   A. Technician A only
   B. Technician B only
   C. Both A and B
   D. Neither A or B

30. Blue-gray smoke comes from the tailpipe of a vehicle during deceleration. Technician A says that this is most likely due to bad valve seals. Technician B says that the cause could be clogged oil return passages. Who is right?
   A. Technician A only
   B. Technician B only
   C. Both A and B
   D. Neither A or B

31. Technician A says that an incorrect ignition pick-up coil gap can cause a misfire. Technician B says that when testing the pick-up coil with an ohmmeter, the meter should read infinity when the ohmmeter is connected to both pick-up coil leads. Who is right?
   A. Technician A only
   B. Technician B only
   C. Both A and B
   D. Neither A or B

32. Hall effect sensors normally produce a:
   A. sine waveform
   B. triangle waveform
   C. sawtooth waveform
   D. square waveform

33. Technician A says that excessive resistance in the voltage side of the charging circuit can cause a low charging rate. Technician B says that too much resistance in the circuit will cause higher than normal voltage drop. Who is right?
   A. Technician A only
   B. Technician B only
   C. Both A and B
   D. Neither A or B

34. The initial timing and spark advance are being checked on an older vehicle with distributor ignition. Technician A says that the engine must be accelerated when checking how much the timing is being advanced by the distributor vacuum advance unit. Technician B says that the vacuum line to the vacuum advance should be disconnected and plugged before checking the ignition timing. Who is right?
   A. Technician A only
   B. Technician B only
   C. Both A and B
   D. Neither A or B

35. Which of the following would cause a spark miss?
   A. high engine temperature
   B. low fuel pressure
   C. dirty throttle body and IAC
   D. distributor cap carbon track

36. All of the following are symptoms of insufficient exhaust gas recirculation EXCEPT:
   A. spark knock
   B. stalling
   C. surging at cruise
   D. increased NOx emissions

37. When testing a catalytic converter with an exhaust pyrometer, the difference between the surface temperatures of the converter inlet and outlet should be _____ with the engine at normal operating temperature.
   A. 50°F (10°C)
   B. 100°F (38°C)
   C. 150°F (66°C)
   D. 200°F (93°C)

38. The EVAP system is designed to:
   A. keep fuel vapors from escaping the fuel tank
   B. capture fuel vapors and route them to the catalytic converter, where they are burned
   C. purge fuel vapors from the charcoal canister to atmosphere
   D. capture fuel vapors and route them to the engine where they become part of the air/fuel mixture and are burned during combustion

Prepare yourself for ASE testing with these questions on
ENGINE PERFORMANCE

39. Which of the following sensors can be checked by measuring the pulse width of the fuel injector?
    A. TP (Throttle Position) sensor
    B. VSS (Vehicle Speed Sensor)
    C. MAF (Mass Air Flow) sensor
    D. CKP (Crankshaft Position) sensor

40. An IAT sensor is being tested. Technician A says that the resistance should be checked on an NTC (Negative Temperature Coefficient) sensor. Technician B says that the voltage drop across the sensor should be checked on this type of sensor. Who is right?
    A. Technician A only
    B. Technician B only
    C. Both A and B
    D. Neither A or B

41. The MAP sensor voltage on a vehicle is measured with the engine running at idle and found to be almost 5 volts. Technician A says that this voltage is too high for idle speed. Technician B says that this voltage will cause the engine to run extremely rich. Who is right?
    A. Technician A only
    B. Technician B only
    C. Both A and B
    D. Neither A or B

42. The engine in a vehicle running at normal operating temperature has a rough idle and black smoke coming from the exhaust. All of the following could be the cause EXCEPT:
    A. EGR valve stuck closed
    B. EVAP canister purge solenoid stuck open
    C. fuel pressure too high
    D. fuel injector(s) stuck open

43. A vehicle is towed in with a 'no start' condition. The technician disconnects the coil wire from the distributor cap, connects a suitable spark tester and checks for a good spark while cranking the engine. If there is no spark, all of the following could be the cause EXCEPT:
    A. a problem in the ignition primary circuit
    B. a problem in the ignition secondary circuit
    C. a bad coil
    D. a bad distributor pick-up coil

44. A technician suspects that a faulty CMP (Camshaft Position) sensor is the cause of a driveability complaint. In order to test the sensor, he must first know what type it is. Since the sensor is equipped with a 3-wire connector, the sensor:
    A. is a Hall effect type
    B. is a magnetic reluctance type
    C. creates a voltage
    D. is a permanent magnet generator

45. An alternator output harness (pigtail) needs to be replaced. Technician A says that a pencil soldering iron should be used to ensure a good connection. Technician B says that a butt splice sleeve connector will be sufficient. Who is right?
    A. Technician A only
    B. Technician B only
    C. Both A and B
    D. Neither A or B

46. Which of the following diagnostic methods can be used to determine which cylinder is leaking combustion chamber gas into the cooling system?
    A. observing the radiator coolant for bubbles while the engine is running
    B. placing a vial of a chemical that is sensitive to combustion gases over the radiator filler neck while the engine is running
    C. holding an exhaust analyzer probe over the radiator filler neck while checking for a reading on the exhaust analyzer
    D. observing the radiator coolant for bubbles while performing a cylinder leakage test

47. A vehicle's tailpipe emissions are being checked with a four-gas exhaust analyzer. The level of CO_2 in the exhaust gas is lower than normal and the level of O_2 is high. Technician A says that the engine has a lean condition. Technician B says that, if the analyzer had five-gas capabilities, the NOx level would be low. Who is right?
    A. Technician A only
    B. Technician B only
    C. Both A and B
    D. Neither A or B

Prepare yourself for ASE testing with these questions on
ENGINE PERFORMANCE

48. A vehicle running at normal operating temperature is idling at too high an idle speed. When checking the IAC (Idle Air Control) valve pintle counts with a scan tool, the reading is zero. Technician A says that the IAC valve is defective. Technician B says that there is a vacuum leak at the intake manifold. Who is right?
   A. Technician A only
   B. Technician B only
   C. Both A and B
   D. Neither A or B

49. A vehicle's exhaust system is being tested for a restriction, using a vacuum gauge connected to the intake manifold. All of the following are indications of a restricted exhaust EXCEPT:
   A. When the engine is gradually accelerated to 2000 RPM, the vacuum reading slowly drops to zero and slowly returns to normal.
   B. When the throttle is closed, the vacuum does not increase.
   C. When the throttle is closed, the vacuum momentarily increases and then resumes the normal reading.
   D. When the engine is accelerated to 2500 RPM, the vacuum reading drops 3 in. Hg below the original reading after a few minutes.

50. Under which of the following conditions is exhaust gas recirculation required?
   A. cold engine at part throttle
   B. warm engine at idle
   C. warm engine at part throttle
   D. warm engine at wide open throttle

51. An electrical circuit is being tested using a DMM (Digital Multimeter). When measuring voltage in the circuit, Technician A says that the meter should be connected in parallel. When measuring amperage, Technician B says that the meter should be connected in series. Who is right?
   A. Technician A only
   B. Technician B only
   C. Both A and B
   D. Neither A or B

52. When retrieving stored codes from a computerized engine control system, a hard fault is found regarding a fuel injector circuit. Technician A says that fuel pressure and volume tests should be performed. Technician B says that the injectors should be replaced on that circuit. Who is right?
   A. Technician A only
   B. Technician B only
   C. Both A and B
   D. Neither A or B

53. A sweep test is being made on a TP sensor using the data from a scan tool. Technician A says this is the preferred method for greatest accuracy. Technician B says that a scope will give the best results. Who is right?
   A. Technician A only
   B. Technician B only
   C. Both A and B
   D. Neither A or B

54. A PCM/ECM is being replaced with a rebuilt unit. Technician A says to disconnect the negative battery cable prior to replacement. Technician B says to test the vehicle driver circuits for low resistance. Who is right?
   A. Technician A only
   B. Technician B only
   C. Both A and B
   D. Neither A or B

55. A technician is testing the ignition on a vehicle with a 'no start' condition. He connects a test light between the negative side of the coil and ground and has an assistant crank the engine. A test light that flutters on and off indicates all of the following **EXCEPT**:
   A. The pickup coil signal is OK.
   B. The ignition module is OK.
   C. The module is triggering the ignition coil to fire.
   D. The coil is OK.

56. Which of the following is used to prevent EGR operation when the engine is cold?
   A. EGR valve position sensor
   B. EGR vacuum solenoid valve
   C. EGR vacuum regulator
   D. Thermal vacuum switch

57. Technician A says that a secondary air injection system forces air into the intake ports. Technician B says that the secondary air injection system reduces spark knock. Who is right?
    A. Technician A only
    B. Technician B only
    C. Both A and B
    D. Neither A or B

58. All of the following are true statements regarding fuel pressure regulators EXCEPT:
    A. With the vacuum line connected to the fuel pressure regulator, fuel pressure should be higher than with the line disconnected.
    B. Most fuel pressure regulators are not adjustable.
    C. Most fuel pressure regulators are connected to manifold vacuum and vary the fuel pressure according to engine load.
    D. Some regulators can suffer from a ruptured diaphragm, allowing fuel to be sucked into the intake manifold through the vacuum line, which operates the regulator, causing a rich running condition.

59. When testing computer-controlled systems, a DMM (Digital Multimeter) should be used with an input impedance of at least:
    A. 10k ohms
    B. 100k ohms
    C. 1 megohm
    D. 10 megohms

60. Technician A says an oscilloscope can be used to read spark plug firing voltage. Technician B says an oscilloscope can be used to check the ignition coil. Who is right?
    A. Technician A only
    B. Technician B only
    C. Both A and B
    D. Neither A or B

61. All of the following are statements describing normal mechanical fan clutch operation EXCEPT:
    A. A fan clutch has viscous drag regardless of temperature.
    B. A fan clutch varies fan speed according to engine temperature.
    C. A fan clutch stops the fan from spinning within two seconds after turning off a hot engine.
    D. A fan clutch varies fan speed according to engine speed.

62. All of the following are indications of a charging system that is undercharging EXCEPT:
    A. slow cranking
    B. dim headlights
    C. short light bulb life
    D. low ammeter indication

63. An engine has a light metallic knocking noise during light engine loads, however, when the cylinder with the noise is disabled during a cylinder balance test, the sound diminishes. Technician A says that the noise is caused by excessive connecting rod bearing clearance. Technician B says that the noise is caused by excessive piston-to-wall clearance. Who is right?
    A. Technician A only
    B. Technician B only
    C. Both A and B
    D. Neither A or B

64. All of the following are true statements regarding intermittent faults EXCEPT:
    A. An intermittent problem is a malfunction that occurred in the past, but is not present at the time of the self-test.
    B. You may have to try to recreate conditions described by the driver to get an intermittent code to reset.
    C. Intermittent problems are often caused by damaged wiring and connectors, so tapping and wiggling wiring harnesses and connectors can sometimes get problems to reoccur and reset codes.
    D. Intermittent faults should be serviced before hard faults.

Prepare yourself for ASE testing with these questions on
ENGINE PERFORMANCE

65. When an EGR valve diaphragm is raised with the engine idling, there is no effect on idle speed. Technician A says that the EGR valve is bad and should be replaced. Technician B says that the EGR passages are clogged with carbon. Who is right?
   A. Technician A only
   B. Technician B only
   C. Both A and B
   D. Neither A or B

66. The MIL is illuminated on a late-model vehicle that is brought in for service. A scan tool is connected to the DLC and the DTC P0107 is obtained. Technician A says that this code indicates a failure in the vehicle's powertrain. Technician B says that this code is manufacturer specific. Who is right?
   A. Technician A only
   B. Technician B only
   C. Both A and B
   D. Neither A or B

67. A vehicle with an AIR system backfires during acceleration. Which of the following should the technician check?
   A. operation of exhaust manifold check valve(s)
   B. output pressure of the air pump
   C. operation of the air bypass valve
   D. the AIR manifolds for restriction

68. A vehicle with a normally closed canister purge solenoid is not purging the EVAP canister when engine operating conditions for purging are met. When the purge solenoid is removed from the vehicle for testing, it allows vacuum flow when voltage is applied. Technician A says the purge solenoid is defective. Technician B says the purge solenoid power circuit is at fault. Who is right?
   A. Technician A only
   B. Technician B only
   C. Both A and B
   D. Neither A or B

69. Two technicians are inspecting an exhaust system. When he taps on the muffler with a mallet, Technician A hears noise coming from inside the muffler and says that it is most likely rotting out from the inside. Technician B says that he hears noise coming from inside the catalytic converter when he taps on it with a mallet and says that the converter is rotting out from the inside. Who is right?
   A. Technician A only
   B. Technician B only
   C. Both A and B
   D. Neither A or B

70. A technician wants to quickly compare the secondary ignition patterns of each cylinder of a V8 engine. Which of the following scope patterns should he use?
   A. primary superimposed
   B. secondary superimposed
   C. parade
   D. raster

71. When manifold vacuum is checked on a vehicle brought in for service it is found to be low but steady. Technician A says that an air/fuel mixture that is too rich can cause this condition. Technician B says that an air/fuel mixture that is too lean can be the cause. Who is right?
   A. Technician A only
   B. Technician B only
   C. Both A and B
   D. Neither A or B

72. A vehicle with multiport fuel injection has a stalling problem. When the throttle body is inspected it is found to be contaminated with sludge buildup. Technician A says that this could be caused by worn rings. Technician B says that this could be caused by a clogged or restricted PCV system. Who is right?
   A. Technician A only
   B. Technician B only
   C. Both A and B
   D. Neither A or B

73. All of the following are indications of a catalytic converter problem EXCEPT:
   A. The converter shell appears bluish.
   B. The converter makes a rattling noise when struck with a mallet.
   C. There is little difference between the inlet and outlet temperatures.
   D. The catalyst monitor signal is stable.

74. All of the following are true of the EVAP canister vent solenoid EXCEPT:
   A. It is activated by the PCM/ECM to allow the flow of fuel vapor from the EVAP canister to the engine.
   B. It is activated by the PCM/ECM to block the entrance of outside air into the canister during the EVAP leak test.
   C. It is used only on vehicles with enhanced EVAP systems.
   D. It is located in the fresh air supply hose to the canister.

75. A vehicle has been towed in with a no-crank condition. The starter solenoid is being tested using a jumper wire between the battery and the solenoid 'S' terminal. Technician A says that if the engine cranks, the problem is in the starter control circuit. Technician B says that if the solenoid makes a clicking sound, it is operating properly and the starter may be defective. Who is right?
   A. Technician A only
   B. Technician B only
   C. Both A and B
   D. Neither A or B

76. All of the following can cause air flow problems through a radiator core EXCEPT:
   A. broken shroud
   B. debris buildup
   C. bent fins
   D. excessive mineral deposits

77. A customer brings his car in because the MIL is on. However, when the vehicle is started in the service bay, the light is off. Technician A says this is because the DTC that turned on the light is no longer in the PCM/ECM's memory. Technician B says this is because the monitor responsible for the DTC has run three times in a row without seeing the same failure. Who is right?
   A. Technician A only
   B. Technician B only
   C. Both A and B
   D. Neither A or B

78. A quick way to determine if valve timing has jumped is to:
   A. look at the timing mark alignment on the cam and crank sprockets
   B. check timing chain or belt slack
   C. check valve movement with the piston at TDC on the exhaust stroke
   D. check valve movement with the engine at TDC on the compression stroke

79. The SFT value on a scan tool is shown with a negative number. Which of the following will also be true?
   A. There is less oxygen in the exhaust
   B. The voltage signal from the oxygen sensor decreased.
   C. The injector pulse width was lengthened.
   D. The SFT value is greater than 1.

80. All of the following could cause a vehicle with enhanced EVAP to fail the PCM/ECM's large leak test EXCEPT:
   A. loose fuel cap
   B. cracked vapor line
   C. stuck open canister vent solenoid
   D. open canister purge valve

Prepare yourself for ASE testing with these questions on
ENGINE PERFORMANCE

81. Two technicians are discussing alcohol in fuel. Technician A says that if any alcohol is mixed with gasoline it will cause driveability problems. Technician B says that excessive amounts of alcohol in fuel can degrade the fuel system. Who is right?
    A. Technician A only
    B. Technician B only
    C. Both A and B
    D. Neither A or B

82. An alcohol in fuel test is being conducted using a 100mL container. If there is 15mL of water in the container at the end of the test, what is the alcohol content of the fuel?
    A. 5 percent
    B. 10 percent
    C. 15 percent
    D. 20 percent

83. Technician A says that a 'pending' code is recorded if monitor results indicate a failure after one drive cycle. Technician B says pending codes should be checked to verify a repair. Who is right?
    A. Technician A only
    B. Technician B only
    C. Both A and B
    D. Neither A or B

84. A voltage generating Vehicle Speed Sensor (VSS) is being tested. Technician A says that the transmission shaft should be rotated and the DC voltage output checked. Technician B says that the sensor resistance should be checked. Who is right?
    A. Technician A only
    B. Technician B only
    C. Both A and B
    D. Neither A or B

85. All of the following can interrupt an OBD II PCM/ECM reprogramming procedure EXCEPT:
    A. getting an automatic virus protection update
    B. opening a door on the vehicle
    C. carrying the vehicle's key fob in your pocket
    D. turning on the ignition key

Standard Brand Presents

THE TURBOCHARGER

FULL-COVERAGE TURBO DOMINATION

TRUSTED QUALITY AND EASIER INSTALLATION
FOR DIESEL AND GASOLINE-POWERED VEHICLES EVERYWHERE

STANDARD®

StandardTurbos.com

Answers to Study-Guide Test Questions

1. The correct answer is A. If a piston ring is leaking, usually a wet compression test will indicate some compression. If a valve is burned, a wet compression test will make no difference and indicate the same compression readings.

2. The correct answer is A. Blue smoke means the engine is burning oil, which could be caused by worn piston rings. Technician B is wrong because a bad head gasket would cause coolant to leak into one or more cylinders, resulting in white exhaust smoke.

3. The correct answer is D. A leaking intake manifold gasket or worn piston rings would not cause a vacuum gauge needle to fluctuate. Worn valve guides would make the needle fluctuate at idle but the needle would steady when engine speed is increased. A weak or broken valve spring will cause a vacuum gauge to fluctuate or jump from low to high readings.

4. The correct answer is B. Advanced ignition timing will cause knock, but retarded timing will not.

5. The correct answer is B. If a vacuum advance mechanism were stuck, the problem would not change if the vacuum hose is connected or disconnected. When the vacuum changes to the vacuum advance mechanism and the distributor plate moves, this may move the wires to the pick-up causing a short or open which would cause the pick-up signal to be lost momentarily.

6. The correct answer is B. To accurately measure spark advance, use a timing light that incorporates an ignition advance meter. The spark advance cannot be determined by listening to the way the engine sounds.

7. The correct answer is C. Checking the vehicle service history may get you pointed in the right direction before you even raise the hood. What repairs have been performed and what parts were installed? What fixed the car before? If it is a recurring problem, maybe a different course of action is in order. If the vehicle really has failed in the same way, checking TSBs may provide information on updated parts that weren't available previously and may solve the problem now. When checking for service campaigns and recalls, you may find that the problem is a defect that the manufacturer will repair.

8. The correct answer is C, both technicians are right. A tapping noise that does not dissipate after the engine warms up could be caused by worn valvetrain components or excessive valvetrain clearance. A similar type noise can sometimes be caused by an exhaust leak at the exhaust manifold/cylinder head juncture.

9. The correct answer is A. A higher-by-comparison spike line on an oscilloscope could indicate a disconnected or open spark plug wire. If a spark plug gap were closed, the oscilloscope would indicate a very low spike line.

10. The correct answer is A. The fuel filter may be in need of service, but it is not the cause of the problem. Unmetered air entering the engine means that there is more air than the amount for which the engine is delivering fuel. A careful examination of the duct between the air flow sensor and the throttle body should reveal where the unmetered air is entering.

11. The correct answer is D, neither technician is right. Although the vehicle may need one of these items before being returned to service, both technicians are jumping to conclusions. A defective crank sensor can cause both of these symptoms, and that is far more likely than either of the other possibilities. The correct action is to test until the defective component is located.

12. The correct answer is C, both technicians are right. Air blowing into the crankcase during a cylinder leakage test indicates a piston, rings and/or cylinder that are worn. When performing a cylinder leakage test, air that causes bubbles in the radiator coolant indicates a cracked head, cracked block, and/or a blown head gasket.

13. The correct answer is B. Before the energy reaches the fuel pump, it must pass through the pump harness, pass-through connector, and the pump wiring. A high resistance in any of these places can keep the pump from running properly. When testing for available pump voltage, remember that there is virtually no load placed on the pump circuit by a multimeter. A test light can load the circuit in place of the pump to determine if there is a resistance, which will cause a significant drop in the voltage available to the pump. A typical resistance in this instance could be relay contacts, which are burned or have insufficient pressure.

Answers to Study-Guide Test Questions

14. The correct answer is A. If the manifold vacuum is low, the fuel pressure regulator will restrict the fuel return and increase the fuel pressure.

15. The correct answer is B. A ported or negative backpressure EGR valve will open when the engine is off and vacuum is applied with a hand operated vacuum pump. A positive backpressure EGR valve needs exhaust backpressure to open. This can be simulated for testing purposes by placing a restriction in the exhaust pipe, starting the engine and placing the transmission in gear. The engine should stall when the restriction created exhaust backpressure builds up enough to open the EGR valve at idle.

16. The correct answer is A. To adjust valve lash for one cylinder's cam lobes, rotate the crankshaft so that its piston is at TDC on the compression stroke. This will position the intake and exhaust valve lifters or cam followers on the base circle of their respective cam lobes. With the engine in this position, the valve lash can be adjusted. Technician B is wrong because hydraulic lifters must be adjusted to position the lifter plunger within the lifter body, therefore the adjuster must be turned further than zero lash.

17. The correct answer is C, both technicians are right. The valve should be removed from the hose and shaken. If the valve rattles when shaken, it is not stuck open or closed. The hose from the intake manifold to the PCV valve is most likely plugged.

18. The correct answer is D. A thermistor is a type of variable resistor that changes resistance according to the change in temperature.

19. The correct answer is D. A thermostat that is stuck open will not allow the engine to come to the correct operating temperature. Heater performance will be poor because the engine coolant will not be hot enough. The ECT will report the lower temperature to the PCM, which will make the air/fuel mixture richer, causing poor fuel economy.

20. The correct answer is C, both technicians are right. Both the oxygen sensor and the intake air temperature sensor relay signals to the PCM/ECM that directly affects the control of fuel.

21. The correct answer is A. The computer reacts to the oxygen sensor signal by adjusting the fuel metering at the injectors. Too high a voltage indicates a rich mixture.

22. The correct answer is A. The sensor measures pulses received per second (Hz) and converts them to revolutions per minute. A constant signal voltage is necessary.

23. The correct answer is A. Although there may be a slight discrepancy in the setting of the TP sensor, it is not relevant to the question. If the coolant temperature sensor tells the PCM/ECM that the engine has not yet warmed up, even though it has, the system will not go into closed loop operation and will run rich.

24. The correct answer is B. The injector would pour fuel even when the cranking had stopped, until the pressure ran out, if the injector was stuck open. In this case, the injector only pours fuel when it is powered up, indicating a shorted driver in the PCM. You can disconnect the injector to double check this, proving that the injector will hold back fuel pressure.

25. The correct answer is D. A wastegate that is stuck closed would cause overboost. A restricted intake duct, a stuck open wastegate, or failed shaft bearings, which would cause the rotating assembly to bind or drag, would all reduce boost pressure and vehicle performance.

26. The correct answer is A. The distinctive pattern described is a normal closed loop, adaptive fuel management pattern. A defective pattern would be a steady high or low voltage when conditions do not dictate that reaction.

27. The correct answer is B. Always use an ammeter to troubleshoot a slow drain in an automotive electrical circuit.

28. The correct answer is A. If an engine cranks slowly and the starter current draw is 90 amps and the voltage is 11 volts, the technician should next check the voltage drop of the starter motor circuit.

Answers to Study-Guide Test Questions

29. The correct answer is A. A cam sensor will have no effect on acceleration. A defective coil pack will break down under the stresses of hard acceleration, and run more smoothly when those stresses are eliminated. However, a roughness in the idle will still be detectable.

30. The correct answer is C, both technicians are right. When a vehicle suffers from worn valve guides and/or bad valve stem seals, you'll see exhaust smoke during deceleration because the high intake vacuum that occurs during deceleration draws the oil through the worn guides or seals. However, before you blame either the valve guides or the valve seals, verify that all of the oil return holes are clean. If oil cannot drain freely back into the crankcase, it can accumulate in the head and be drawn by vacuum into the combustion chamber, causing exhaust smoke.

31. The correct answer is A. Pick-up coil gap that is too small or too large may cause engine misfire. Technician B is wrong because the normal resistance reading is 500 to 1500 ohms when an ohmmeter is connected to the pick-up coil leads. The ohmmeter should read infinity when the ohmmeter leads are connected to ground and either pick-up coil connector lead.

32. The correct answer is D. Hall effect sensors produce a square wave pattern. Sine waveforms are produced by two-wire, reluctor (permanent magnet) sensors.

33. The correct answer is C, both technicians are right. Excessive resistance in the voltage and/or ground sides of the charging circuit can cause a low charging rate due to the difference between alternator output and electrical system voltage requirements. The voltage available at any point in the circuit depends on the circuit resistance. The higher the resistance, the more voltage is needed to force current through the circuit. A high voltage reading when performing a voltage drop test is a sign of too much resistance.

34. The correct answer is B. Initial timing can be adjusted on these systems after the vacuum hose is disconnected from the advance unit and plugged. Technician A is wrong because the engine must be accelerated only to check mechanical advance. The vacuum advance unit can be checked using a timing light and a vacuum pump. Check the timing advance while applying vacuum to the advance unit with the pump.

35. The correct answer is D. If the power is diverted to ground before reaching the spark plug, a spark miss will result.

36. The correct answer is B. Stalling is a symptom of too much EGR or EGR at the wrong time.

37. The correct answer is B. A simple test for whether a catalytic converter is functioning properly is by measuring the inlet and outlet temperatures. With the engine at normal operating temperature, check the temperature of the exhaust inlet and outlet surface before and after the converter using a temperature probe and a DMM or an exhaust pyrometer. The exhaust surface temperature should be at least 100°F (38°C) hotter than the intake surface temperature. If not, the converter is probably not operating at peak efficiency.

38. The correct answer is D. The purpose of the evaporative emissions control system (EVAP) is to prevent HC emissions from escaping the fuel system to atmosphere. Prior to the introduction of EVAP systems, fuel vaporized and was emitted to the atmosphere from vented gas caps and carburetor float bowls, polluting the environment. The EVAP system is designed to capture these vapors and route them to the engine where they become part of the air/fuel mixture and are burned during combustion.

39. The correct answer is C. Pulse width is a measurement of how long the fuel injector is open, or how much fuel the fuel injector is delivering. The longer the PCM/ECM grounds the injector, the longer the injector sprays. The longer the injector sprays, the richer the mixture becomes. The less the injector sprays, the leaner the mixture. Restrict the air intake and look for a change in fuel control. If a change in fuel delivery is noticed, the MAF sensor is most likely working properly.

40. The correct answer is C, both technicians are right. Resistance varies inversely with temperature on an NTC sensor. The sensor's function is usually checked by measuring the resistance between the sensor terminals. Most manufacturers publish resistance/temperature tables, but in general the resistance should be approximately 3000 ohms at room temperature (70°F, or 21°C). Start the engine, and as it warms up check that the values change smoothly, or heat the sensor using a hair dryer to see if the values change smoothly. If the resistance value doesn't change, the

Answers to Study-Guide Test Questions

sensor is probably defective. The sensor can also be checked by measuring voltage drop. More voltage is dropped across the sensor when it is cold, and less when hot. The PCM/ECM, by monitoring the voltage change, adjusts the amount of fuel injection according to the air temperature. With the sensor installed, back-probe the sensor terminals with a voltmeter connected across the sensor terminals. Compare the voltage readings at various temperatures with the manufacturer's voltage/temperature table. The voltage drop can also be seen using a scan tool.

41. The correct answer is C, both technicians are right. A high voltage reading at the MAP sensor should indicate atmospheric pressure inside the intake manifold, which should only happen when the engine is off or at WOT (Wide Open Throttle). Since the engine is running, the PCM/ECM will think the engine is at WOT and richen the fuel mixture accordingly.

42. The correct answer is A. An EGR valve that is stuck closed could cause spark knock or other drive-ability problems, but would not cause rough idle and black smoke. An EVAP canister purge solenoid that was stuck open could be the cause because it would cause the canister to improperly purge at idle. High fuel pressure could be the problem because it would cause more fuel to be injected per injector opening. Fuel injectors that were stuck open would allow fuel flow when they were not energized and could also be the cause of the problem.

43. The correct answer is B. There would only be a problem in the ignition secondary circuit if there were a good spark. If there is no spark, the problem is in the primary circuit. Since the primary windings of the coil and the distributor pick-up coil are part of the primary circuit, they are possible causes of a no-spark condition.

44. The correct answer is A. Hall Effect switches are equipped with a 3-wire connector. Magnetic reluctance types are equipped with a 2-wire connector. They create a voltage and are also known as PM (Permanent Magnet) generators.

45. The correct answer is D, neither technician is right. A pencil iron will not produce sufficient heat to maintain the necessary temperature to melt and flow the solder to properly join the wires. Technician B is incorrect because the sleeves, even when crimped, will develop resistance and cause overheating of the wires, leading to failure at the alternator connection.

46. The correct answer is D. While each of these methods can be used to determine whether there is a combustion chamber leak into the cooling system, only a cylinder leakage test will identify which cylinder is leaking.

47. The correct answer is A. Any deviation, rich or lean, from the optimum air/fuel ratio will cause the CO_2 level in the exhaust to drop. Higher O_2 levels indicate a lean mixture, while lower levels mean a richer mixture. Technician B is wrong because lean air/fuel mixtures can cause high levels of NOx in the exhaust.

48. The correct answer is B. Zero counts corresponds to a closed IAC valve passage, which the PCM/ECM would signal to try to close off the air flow, so Technician A is wrong. Since the IAC valve is closed, the high idle speed is most likely caused by air entering from another location, such as a vacuum leak.

49. The correct answer is C. When the throttle is closed on a properly operating vehicle with a good exhaust system, the vacuum should momentarily increase and then resume the normal reading. All of the other answers describe indications of a restricted exhaust system.

50. The correct answer is C. When the engine is warm and above idle speed, EGR is required to prevent spark knock and reduce NOx emissions. Until the engine is warm, there is no need for exhaust gas recirculation because combustion is still sufficiently cool. Even when the engine is warm, there is no need for exhaust gas recirculation at idle because combustion pressures are relatively low and NOx is not formed, and exhaust gas recirculation would stall the engine because of too much dilution. At WOT, the need for power outweighs the need to control NOx emissions, and since WOT needs richer, and therefore slightly cooler mixtures, NOx formation is minimal anyway.

51. The correct answer is C, both technicians are right. A voltmeter is always connected in parallel when making a voltage check of a circuit. An ammeter is

Answers to Study-Guide Test Questions

connected in series with the circuit, so all the current passing through passes through the ammeter.

52. The correct answer is D, neither technician is right. Technician A is wrong because a problem with fuel pressure and volume would not set a fuel injector circuit code. Technician B is wrong because the code indicated a malfunction in the fuel injector circuit, and replacing the injectors would be jumping to the conclusion that the injectors are bad. The circuit should be tested in the order specified by the manufacturer's diagnostic procedures before any components are replaced.

53. The correct answer is B. Erratic readings or a momentary infinite reading indicates a defective sensor. Since the processed data of a scan tool can 'skip' several moments during the sweep, allowing dropouts to be 'hidden' during the time between updates of screen data, the voltage test of a TP sensor is best accomplished using a scope, as even the smallest dropouts can be easily seen as the throttle is moved.

54. The correct answer is C, both technicians are right. Use the checklist provided with the rebuilt unit to test the circuits that will connect to drivers in the new PCM/ECM, to be certain that no circuits will draw excessive current.

55. The correct answer is D. The test light fluttering on and off means that the coil is being triggered to fire, it is not a test of the coil itself.
56. The correct answer is D. A TVS (Thermal Vacuum Switch) is used to prevent EGR when the engine is cold. If the switch is operating properly, it should not allow vacuum flow until the engine reaches a specific operating temperature.

57. The correct answer is D, neither technician is right. The secondary air injection system injects air into the exhaust system. Since the secondary air injection system is used after the combustion event, it cannot reduce spark knock.

58. The correct answer is A. With the vacuum line connected to the fuel pressure regulator, fuel pressure should be lower than with the line disconnected.

59. The correct answer is D. For maximum protection to the computer-controlled system or any electronic circuit, it is best to use at least a 10-megohm impedance DMM.

60. The correct answer is C, both technicians are right. The spark plug firing voltage can be determined as well as the condition of the ignition coil by using an oscilloscope.

61. The correct answer is D. A properly operating fan clutch will change the speed of the fan according to engine temperature. When the engine is cold, the fan clutch does not turn the fan very fast, even when engine speed is increased. As the engine warms up, the fan clutch increases the speed of the fan. If the fan speed varies only according to engine speed, regardless of temperature, then the fan clutch is probably seized and should be replaced.

62. The correct answer is C. Overcharging is indicated by short light bulb life and a battery that continually needs water.

63. The correct answer is A. When you eliminate the ignition or injection to a cylinder with a rod knock, the sound diminishes. Unlike a connecting rod bearing noise, piston slap does not quiet down and may in fact grow louder when you eliminate ignition or fuel injection to that cylinder.

64. The correct answer is D. Hard faults should be serviced before intermittent faults.

65. The correct answer is B. Manually raising the EGR diaphragm when the engine is idling should allow exhaust gas into the intake air stream, which should stall an engine at idle. Since this had no effect on the idle speed, we know that there is no exhaust gas flow, so replacing the EGR valve would have no effect. Technician B is correct because the lack of exhaust gas flow is most likely caused by carbon buildup in the EGR passages.

66. The correct answer is A. Technician A is right because the alpha character indicates the area of the vehicle where the failure occurred: B for Body, C for Chassis, P for Powertrain, and U for Network. Technician B is wrong because Manufacturer specific codes have the number 1 as the first digit. DTC P0107 has a zero as the first digit, so it is a generic code, common to all manufacturers.

67. The correct answer is C. The air bypass valve momentarily exhausts the air pump's output by diverting it to the atmosphere during engine acceleration. During acceleration, the fuel injectors inject more fuel, providing a richer mixture. If oxygen is pumped into the exhaust manifold during this time, a backfire results when the excess hydrocarbons are burned.

68. The correct answer is B. A normally closed purge solenoid should allow vacuum flow when activated by the PCM/ECM, so the purge solenoid is functioning properly. If the purge solenoid is being commanded by the PCM/ECM, then the problem is in the power supply to the purge solenoid.

69. The correct answer is A. When inspecting an exhaust system, tap on the muffler with a mallet and listen for the sound of loose rust particles. Mufflers usually rot out from the inside, so even if the outside of the muffler appears OK, it still may be ready for replacement. Technician B is incorrect because if a rattling sound is heard coming from a catalytic converter when it is struck with a mallet, it means that the ceramic substrate has come loose and is disintegrating.

70. The correct answer is B. Answer A is wrong because the technician wants to see the secondary ignition pattern. The secondary superimposed pattern places all patterns on top of one another to check for uniformity. Any pattern that does not align with the others can indicate a problem with that cylinder. Once a problem cylinder has been identified, the other patterns can then be used to determine which component is causing the problem.

71. The correct answer is C, both technicians are right. When the idle vacuum is low but steady, suspect an air/fuel mixture that is too lean or too rich. Air leaks or vacuum leaks can cause a lean condition and are common causes of rough idle, hesitation, stalling and hard starting. If the mixture is artificially enriched by injecting propane into the induction system, an engine

running lean should speed up and the vacuum reading should rise. If the air/fuel mixture is too rich, the engine will slow down and the vacuum reading will drop. If the engine is running lean and you suspect a vacuum leak as the cause, try using a propane kit with a length of hose attached to find the leak. Pass the hose end around the suspected areas and listen for a change in idle.

72. The correct answer is C, both technicians are right. The PCM/ECM bases idle speed calculations on a set amount of air that bypasses the throttle plates. If this air flow is reduced by accumulated sludge deposits, these calculations will be incorrect and may result in stalling. Worn rings can cause excessive blowby into the crankcase. Excessive blowby can be more than the PCV system can handle, so instead of going into the intake manifold, these gases force their way through the fresh air intake and into the air cleaner. Oil deposits that are part of the crankcase gases can then accumulate on the throttle body when these gases mix with the air entering the engine, eventually causing the sludge buildup. A clogged or restricted PCV valve can cause the same results.

73. The correct answer is D. If the signal from the catalyst monitor fluctuates high and low like the signal from the primary oxygen sensor, it means that the converter is not functioning properly. All of the other answers are indicators of catalytic converter problems. If the converter shell appears bluish, it means that the converter has overheated. If the converter rattles inside when struck with a mallet, it means that the ceramic substrate has come loose and is disintegrating. The exhaust surface temperature should be hotter than the intake surface temperature. If not, the converter is probably not operating at peak efficiency.

74. The correct answer is A. The canister purge solenoid, not the vent solenoid, is activated by the PCM to allow the flow of fuel vapor from the EVAP canister to the engine.

75. The correct answer is C, both technicians are right. The solenoid would be defective in this test if it made no noise and did not click or activate the starter.

76. The correct answer is D. Excessive mineral deposits can restrict coolant flow through the radiator, but would have no effect on air flow. A broken fan shroud would cause less than optimal air flow through the radiator core. Debris and bent fins would block air flow through the core.

77. The correct answer is B. Technician A is wrong because the DTC will remain the PCM/ECM's memory until a specific number of warmup cycles have been completed.

78. The correct answer is C. With the piston at TDC on the exhaust stroke, both valves should be open slightly because of valve overlap. The exhaust valve should close a few degrees after TDC and the intake valve should open a few degrees before. If the valves do not operate this way with the crankshaft at this position, the valve timing is incorrect. Answer A is wrong because, while this way will achieve a determination, it will most likely take longer to disassemble the front of the engine. Answer B is wrong because looseness in the belt or chain can indicate a strong possibility that the valve timing has jumped, but is not confirmation of the condition.

79. The correct answer is A. An SFT with a negative number means the injector pulse width was shortened, so answer C is wrong. A shortened injector pulse width means that the SFT value was decreased below 1, so answer D is wrong. The SFT will decrease in response to an increased voltage signal from the oxygen sensor, so answer B is wrong. A rich mixture, one with less oxygen, will increase the voltage signal from the oxygen sensor.

80. The correct answer is D. The PCM/ECM opens the canister purge valve to cause a vacuum in the EVAP system. All of the other answers are leaks that would prevent a vacuum from being created.

81. The correct answer is B. If an excessive amount of alcohol is mixed with gasoline in vehicles not designed for it, it can degrade rubber fuel system components, clog the fuel filter and cause a lean air/fuel mixture. Technician A is wrong because gasoline mixed with up to 10% alcohol (ethanol) is used in many parts of the U.S. The small percentage of alcohol is generally used to increase the octane rating and decrease carbon monoxide emissions.

82. The correct answer is A. To test the alcohol content of fuel, fill a 100mL container to the 90mL mark with fuel, then fill to the 100mL mark with water. Close the container and shake vigorously for 10-15 seconds, then allow the contents to settle. Any alcohol that is in the gasoline will be absorbed by the water and settle to the bottom of the container. If there is now 15mL of water in the container, there was 5% alcohol in the fuel.

83. The correct answer is C, both technicians are right. A 'trip' is a completed drive cycle. Although some monitors will set a DTC and turn on the MIL if a fault is found after one trip, for most DTCs the PCM/ECM must see the same fault occur during two trips. After the first trip, the fault is recorded as 'pending'. Once the PCM/ECM sees the same fault the next time the monitor runs, the PCM will turn on the MIL. If the same fault is not seen during the next monitor, the pending code will be cleared. Once repairs are completed, operate the vehicle in a manner necessary to satisfy the drive cycle requirements for the monitor that set the DTC. Recheck the monitor status and check for pending codes to see if the fault returned.

84. The correct answer is B. Technician B is correct because the amount of resistance in a VSS can be checked with an ohmmeter. Technician A is incorrect because when VSS voltage is checked, the meter should be on the AC setting. The VSS is a permanent magnet generator that produces an AC signal. When checked with a lab scope, this signal will appear as a sine wave pattern.

85. The correct answer is D. Interrupting a PCM/ECM reprogramming procedure can cause the process to fail and possibly ruin the PCM/ECM. Getting an automatic update for virus protection software on the PC could interrupt the process, as could opening a door on the vehicle and turning on the interior lights. Many vehicles have security systems that automatically activate when you walk a certain distance from the vehicle. The proximity device is usually incorporated in the key-fob, so carrying it in your pocket could activate the security system and interrupt the reprogramming process. Turning on the ignition key would not interrupt reprogramming and is usually required at some point.

Notes

Glossary of Terms

AC - see alternating current.

actuator - a control device that delivers mechanical action in response to a vacuum or electrical signal; anything that the engine control computer uses to do something, such as trigger fuel injection or fire a spark plug. Most actuators on a computer-controlled engine system are activated by grounding their circuits rather than by actively powering them, since that protects the computer from short circuits.

air duct - a tube, channel or other tubular structure used to carry air to a specific location.

air gap - a specified space between two components. Space or gap between spark plug electrodes, motor and generator armatures and field shoes. The space or gap between the compressor drive hub and pulley assembly.

air injection reaction (AIR) system - a system that provides fresh air to the exhaust system under controlled conditions to reduce emissions. The air source can be a pulse-air pump or an electrically or belt driven pump. Upstream air injection goes into the exhaust manifold to assist in after-burning HC laden exhaust gases. Downstream air injection goes into the oxidation bed of the catalytic converter to help oxidize HC and CO emissions.

air/fuel ratio - the proportion of air to fuel by weight in the fuel mixture drawn into the engine.

air pump - device to produce a flow of air at higher-than-atmospheric pressure. Normally referred to as a thermactor air supply pump.

alloy - a mixture of different metals (e.g., solder, an alloy consisting of lead and tin).

alternating current (AC) - electric current that flows in one direction, from positive to negative, and then reverses direction, from negative to positive.

alternator - a belt driven device that provides electrical current for the vehicle's charging system; a device that converts mechanical energy into electrical energy; a generating device that uses diode rectifiers to convert AC to DC.

ambient temperature - the temperature of the air surrounding an object.

ammeter - an instrument for measuring the strength of electrical current flow in a circuit in terms of amperes.

amp - see ampere.

amperage - the amount of electrical current flowing in a circuit.

ampere (amp) - a unit for measuring the strength (rate of flow) of an electrical current.

amplifier - a circuit or device used to increase the voltage or current of a signal.

amplify - to enlarge or strengthen original characteristics; usually used in reference to electronics.

analog - in automotive terms, a device, such as a gauge, that uses a needle and printed references, rather than an electronic readout.

analog computer - a microprocessor that uses similar electrical signals to make its calculations.

antifreeze - a material such as ethylene glycol, which is added to water to lower its freezing point; used in an automobile's cooling system.

arcing - electrical energy jumping across a gap.

armature - a laminated, soft iron core wrapped by wire that converts electrical energy to mechanical energy.

atmospheric pressure - the pressure exerted on an object by the weight of the earth's atmosphere. At sea level, 14.7 psi (101 kPa), less at higher altitudes.

atomization - the breaking down of a fluid into a fine mist that can be suspended in air.

backfire - the sudden combustion of gasses in the intake or exhaust manifold, resulting in a loud explosion.

backlash - the clearance or play between two parts, as in gear mesh.

backpressure - pressure created by a blockage or restriction in an exhaust system.

ballast resistor - resistor in the primary side of the ignition system that is used to reduce voltage by approximately 4-5 volts.

Training for Certification   105

barometric pressure - the pressure of the atmosphere, usually expressed in terms of the height of a column of mercury. A sensor or its signal circuit sends a varying frequency signal to the processor relating actual barometric pressure.

base circle - the part of a camshaft lobe that is opposite the tip of the nose. The part of the camshaft lobe that does not move the valve in any way.

battery - a device that produces electricity through electrochemical action.

battery acid - the sulfuric acid solution used as the electrolyte in a battery.

battery cell - the part of a storage battery made from two dissimilar metals and an acid solution. A cell stores chemical energy to be used later as electrical energy.

bearing clearance - the amount of space left between a shaft and the bearing surface for lubricating oil to enter.

before top dead center (BTDC) - the degrees of crankshaft rotation just before the piston in a specific cylinder reaches TDC, the highest point in its vertical travel on the compression stroke. On most vehicles, spark occurs a certain number of degrees of crankshaft rotation BTDC.

bendix drive - the starter drive gear that is attached to the starter motor armature and engages the gear teeth on the flywheel.

bimetallic - two kinds of metal, with different thermal expansion rates, that when attached to one another, the resulting assembly will bend in the direction of the metal that expands the least.

blowby - the unburned fuel and products of combustion that leak past the piston rings and into the crankcase at the last part of the combustion stroke.

boost pressure - term used when a turbocharger increases the air pressure entering an engine above atmospheric pressure.

brush - a bar of conductive material that rides on the commutator of a generator or motor.

BTDC - see before top dead center.

--c--

calculated load value - the percentage of engine capacity being used, calculated by the ECM or PCM based on current air flow divided by known maximum air consumption of the particular engine under test. Displayed as a percentage on scan tools, labeled ENG LOAD.

calibrate - to adjust a tool to achieve accuracy of measurement.

camshaft - a shaft with eccentric lobes that control the opening of the intake and exhaust valves.

camshaft follower - on OHC engines the equivalent of a rocker arm.

camshaft lobe - the eccentric on a camshaft that acts on lifters or followers and in turn, other valvetrain components as the camshaft is rotated, to open the intake and exhaust valves.

camshaft position sensor (CMP) - a magnetic reluctance or Hall effect sensor, usually mounted internally in the engine to inform the ECM or PCM of piston position on the intake stroke for timing and synchronization of sequential fuel injection.

camshaft sprocket - the sprocket on a camshaft that is turned by a chain or belt from the crankshaft. The camshaft sprocket has twice as many teeth as the crankshaft sprocket.

capacitor - a device, made up of two or more conducting plates, separated by an insulator, used to store an electric surge or charge of current.

carbon - a hard or soft nonmetallic element that forms in an engine's combustion chamber when oil is burned.

carbon dioxide (CO2) - a colorless, odorless, noncombustible gas, heavier than air; can be compressed into a super-cold solid known as dry ice; changes from solid to vapor at −78.5°C.

carbon monoxide (CO) - a colorless, odorless gas, which is highly poisonous. CO is produced by incomplete combustion. It is absorbed by the bloodstream 400 times faster than oxygen.

carburetor - a device that atomizes air and fuel in a proportion that is burnable in the engine.

catalyst - a compound or substance that can speed up or slow down the reaction of other substances without being consumed itself. In a catalytic converter, special metals (platinum or palladium) are used to promote combustion of unburned hydrocarbons and reduce carbon monoxide.

catalytic converter - an emission control device located in the exhaust system that contains catalysts, which reduce hydrocarbons, carbon monoxide and nitrogen oxides in the exhaust gases.

CCA - see cold cranking amps.

Celsius - the basis of the metric system of temperature measurement in which water's boiling point is 100ºC and its freezing point is 0ºC.

charge - the electrical current that passes through the battery to restore it to full power; to fill, or bring up to the specific level, an A/C system with refrigerant; the required amount of refrigerant for an A/C system.

charging system - the system that supplies electrical power for vehicle operation and recharges the battery.

check valve - a gate or valve that allows passage of gas or fluid in one direction only.

choke - a device used on carbureted vehicles to reduce the amount of air entering the intake manifold while leaving the amount of fuel unchanged. The purpose of a choke is to richen the mixture enough that a cold engine can still get enough vaporized fuel to start.

circuit - a path through which electricity flows before returning to its source.

circuit breaker - a device used in an electrical circuit to interrupt current flow in the event of an overload or short.

CKP sensor - see crankshaft position sensor.

clear flood mode - a situation in which, under certain circumstances, the computer will shut off all fuel injection or greatly reduce it. If the throttle position (TP) sensor reports wide-open throttle (80 percent open, 3.7 volts or more) and if the engine speed is below 400 rpm, this combination of sensor inputs will be interpreted as an attempt by the driver to 'clear flood,' that is to blow puddled gasoline off the spark plugs to enable the vehicle to start. This can cause a no-start problem if someone tries to start the engine with the pedal fully depressed, or if the throttle position (TP) sensor loses its ground.

clearance - the specified distance between two components.

closed loop - electronic feedback system in which sensors provide constant information on what is taking place in the engine; the state of the engine control computer system when it is working normally, at full operating temperature and normal speeds with the oxygen sensor switching. The fuel injection quantity is determined by the set of inputs from the engine control computer's sensors, most specifically the oxygen sensor in the exhaust stream. A closed loop system samples its output and uses that sampling to modify the next inputs.

CMP sensor - see camshaft position sensor.

CO - see carbon monoxide.

CO2 - see carbon dioxide.

cold cranking amps (CCA) - the amount of cranking amperes that a battery can deliver in 30 seconds at 0˚F (–18˚C).

combustion - the burning of the air/fuel mixture.

combustion chamber - enclosure formed by a pocket in the cylinder head and the top of the piston, where the spark plug ignites the compressed air/fuel mixture. The volume of the cylinder above the piston when the piston is at TDC.

commutator - a slotted ring located at the end of the armature of a generator or motor. The commutator provides the electrical connection between the armature and brushes.

compound - a mixture of two or more ingredients.

compression - in a solid material, compression is the opposite of tension. In a gas, compression causes the gas to be confined in a smaller area, raising its temperature and pressure.

compression ratio - ratio of the volume in the cylinder above the piston when the piston is at bottom dead center to the volume in the cylinder above the piston when the piston is at top dead center.

compression stroke - the second stroke of the 4-stroke engine cycle, in which the piston moves from bottom dead center and the intake valve is closed, trapping and compressing the air/fuel mixture in the cylinder.

computer - an electrical device that receives information from sensors and makes decisions based on these inputs along with programmed information, and sends out the decisions to actuators.

concentric - two or more circles that have a common center.

conductor - a material that provides a path for the flow of electrical current or heat.

continuity - the condition that exists in a working electrical circuit. A circuit that is unbroken, not open.

continuous injection system - a system that uses fuel under pressure to modulate or change the fuel injection area.

contraction - reduction in mass or dimension; the opposite of expansion.

coolant - mixture of water and ethylene glycol-based antifreeze that circulates through the engine to help maintain proper temperatures.

cooling fan - a mechanically or electrically driven propeller that draws air through the radiator.

cooling system - the system used to remove excess heat from an engine and transfer it to the atmosphere. Includes the radiator, cooling fan, hoses, water pump, thermostat and engine coolant passages.

core - in automotive terminology, the main part of a heat exchanger, such as a radiator, evaporator or heater. Usually made of tubes, surrounded by cooling fins, used to transfer heat from the coolant to the air.

crankshaft position sensor (CKP) - a magnetic reluctance or Hall effect sensor, usually mounted internally in the engine, externally to the engine or in the distributor to inform the ECM or PCM of crankshaft position, location of No. 1 piston, and crankshaft speed for ignition timing and other calculations needed by the system where rpm is an input.

crossflow radiator - a radiator in which coolant enters on one side, travels through tubes, and collects on the opposite side.

current - the flow or rate of flow of an electric charge through a conductor or medium between two points having a different potential, expressed in amperes.

cylinder balance test - an engine diagnostic test used to compare the power output of all the engine's cylinders. Also known as a power contribution test.

cylinder leakage test - an engine diagnostic test where the piston in the cylinder to be tested is brought to top dead center (TDC) on the compression stroke and compressed air is pumped into the cylinder through the spark plug hole. Where the air leaks out shows the location of the compression leak. A leakage tester will compare the air leaking out of the cylinder to the amount of air being put into it, expressed as a percentage.

--d--

dampen - to slow or reduce oscillations or movement.

data link connector (DLC) - a means through which information about the state of the vehicle control system can be extracted with a scan tool. This information includes actual readouts on each sensor's input circuit and some actuator signals. It also includes any trouble codes stored. The data link connector is also used to disable the computer's ignition timing adjustments on some engines so base or reference timing can be measured with a timing light. Before OBD II, each OEM had a unique data link connector and called it by a different name. With the advent of OBD II, the DLC became standardized as a 16-pin connector to which the scan tool could be connected to read data and sometimes control outputs of the PCM/ECM.

DC - see direct current.

dead center - the extreme upper or lower position of the crankshaft throw at which the piston is not moving in either direction.

deck - top of the engine block where the cylinder head is mounted.

deflection - bending or movement away from the normal position due to loading.

density - the ratio of the mass of an object to its volume.

detonation - abnormal combustion of an air fuel mixture. When pressure in the cylinder becomes excessive and the mixture explodes violently, instead of burning in a controlled manner. The sound of detonation can be heard as the cylinder walls vibrate. Detonation is sometimes confused with preignition or ping.

diagnostic trouble code (DTC) - a code that represents

and can be used to identify a malfunction in a computer control system.

dial caliper - versatile instrument capable of taking inside, outside, depth and step measurements.

dial indicator - a measuring device equipped with a readout dial used most often to determine end motion or irregularities.

diaphragm - flexible, impermeable membrane on which pressure acts to produce mechanical movement; in automotive terminology, any disc-shaped device; can be as diverse as thin membranes that separate two chambers in a component, and large metal discs that activate clutch pressure plates.

dieseling - a condition by which hot spots in the combustion chamber(s) cause the engine to run on after the key is turned off.

digital - a voltage signal that uses on and off pulses.

digital multimeter (DMM) - an instrument that measures volts, ohms and amps and displays the results numerically.

dilution - to make thinner or weaker. Oil is diluted by the addition of fuel and water droplets.

diode - a simple semiconductor device that permits flow of electricity in one direction but not the other.

direct current (DC) - electric current that flows in one direction.

direct ignition - a distributorless ignition system in which spark distribution is controlled by the vehicle's computer.

direct injection - a fuel injection system wherein fuel is sprayed directly into the combustion chamber, that is, no precombustion chambers or manifold injection.

disable - a microcomputer decision that results in an automotive system being deactivated.

discharge - the flow of current from a battery; to remove the refrigerant from an air conditioning system.

displacement - the volume of a cylinder displaced by the piston as it moves from TDC to BDC (a complete stroke).

distributor - part of the distributor ignition system that triggers the spark and directs it through the wires to the spark plugs.

distributor ignition - an ignition system that uses a distributor, electronically controlled or not.

distributorless ignition - see electronic ignition.

DLC - see data link connector.

DMM - see digital multimeter.

downflow radiator - a radiator in which coolant enters the top of the radiator and is drawn downward by gravity.

driveability - the degree to which a vehicle operates properly, including starting, running smoothly, accelerating and delivering reasonable fuel mileage.

dropping resistor - battery voltage reduction device.

DTC - see diagnostic trouble code.

duration - the length of time that a valve remains open, measured in crankshaft degrees.

duty cycle - a signal that varies the ratio of on time to off time, resulting in a square wave that can range between zero and 100 percent or may be high or low, and off may be high or low; in a process, the ratio of on time to total cycle time; in fuel injectors, the percentage of on-time to total cycle time; in solenoids, the percentage of on-time to total cycle time.

dwell time - degree of crankshaft rotation during which the primary circuit is on.

--e--

eccentric - a rotating part of a shaft that is set off-center of the axis; the part of a camshaft that operates the mechanical fuel pump.
ECM - see engine control module.

ECT sensor - see engine coolant temperature sensor.

efficiency - ratio of the amount of energy put into an engine compared to the amount of energy coming out of the engine; a measure of how well a particular machine works; the ratio of effective work to the amount of energy expended in producing it; output divided by input equals efficiency.

EGR - see exhaust gas recirculation system.

EGR valve - see exhaust gas recirculation (EGR) valve.

EGR valve position sensor - a sensor mounted on the EGR valve that signals the engine control computer regarding EGR valve pintle position and EGR flow.

electrode - a terminal that conducts an electric current into or away from the conducting part of a circuit, such as the terminal of a battery; firing terminals found in a spark plug.

electrolysis - chemical and electrical decomposition process that can damage metals such as brass, copper and aluminum in the cooling system; the decomposition of an electrolyte by the action of an electric current passing through it.

electrolyte - a material whose atoms become ionized (electrically charged) in solution. In automobiles, the battery electrolyte is a mixture of sulfuric acid and water.

electromagnet - an iron core surrounded by a coil of wire that temporarily becomes a magnet when an electric current flows through the wire.

electromagnetic induction - moving a wire through a magnetic field to create current flow in the wire.

electromechanical - refers to a device that incorporates both electrical and mechanical principles together in its operation.

electronic - pertaining to the control of systems or devices by the use of small electrical signals and various semiconductor devices and circuits.

electronic control unit (ECU) - the computer in an electronic control system.

electronic ignition (EI) - an ignition system that does not use a distributor, but instead has coils dedicated to individual spark plugs or pairs of spark plugs. Referred to as distributorless ignition, direct ignition, coil near plug ignition or coil over plug ignition. A system in which the timing and firing of the spark plugs is controlled by an electronic control unit.

emitter - in a transistor, the region or layer of semiconductor material from which electrons are injected into the base region.

energy - the capacity for doing work and overcoming resistance.

engine control module (ECM) - the electronic computer that controls engine operation. ECM is synonymous with ECA, ECU, SBEC or SMEC. It is less powerful than the PCM (Powertrain Control Module) or VCM (Vehicle Control Module) in that it controls only engine operation.

engine coolant temperature (ECT) sensor - a sensor that works by a negative coefficient thermistor, which loses resistance as its temperature goes up (just like the intake air temperature sensor). When the computer applies its 5-volt reference signal to the sensor, this voltage is reduced through a ground circuit by an amount corresponding to the temperature of the engine coolant.

ethanol - a widely-used gasoline additive known for its abilities as an octane enhancer.

EVAP - see evaporative emission system.

evaporation - the process through which a liquid is turned into vapor.

evaporative emission (EVAP) canister - a charcoal-filled container with lines to the top of the fuel tank, to the intake manifold and to the air cleaner. The charcoal element adsorbs fuel vapors from the gas tank and stores them until the engine is running at normal operating temperatures and speeds. Then, a valve between the canister and engine opens, fresh air is drawn in through the canister air filter, and the air and fuel vapors are drawn into the engine and burned, purging the canister.

evaporative emission (EVAP) canister purge solenoid - EVAP canister purging is controlled by the engine control computer, which determines when the canister should be purged based on various sensor inputs. When purging is needed the computer operates the purge solenoid, which controls the vacuum to purge the canister. Generally, the purge solenoid is activated when the engine is running above idle speed and at normal operating temperature.

evaporative emission (EVAP) canister purge valve - a valve on the line between the EVAP canister and the intake manifold. When the engine is running, under certain operating conditions, the valve opens, fresh air is drawn in through the canister air filter, and the air and fuel vapors are drawn into the engine and burned, purging the canister.

Glossary of Terms

evaporative emission (EVAP) system - an emission control system that prevents HC emissions from escaping the fuel system to atmosphere.

excessive wear - in mechanical terms, wear of a component that exceeds designed limits; wear caused by overloading a part that is in an out-of-balance condition, resulting in lower-than-normal life expectancy of the part being subjected to the adverse operating condition.

exhaust gas recirculation (EGR) system - helps prevent the formation of oxides of nitrogen (NOx) by recirculating a certain amount of exhaust as an inert gas through the intake manifold to keep the peak combustion temperatures below what would form those chemical compounds. The computer determines when and how much exhaust to recirculate based on information from all its other sensors. It then actuates the EGR solenoid, which opens a vacuum circuit or operates an electronic circuit to actually work the EGR valve. The computer uses a duty-cycle (percentage of on-time) signal to activate the solenoid.

exhaust gas recirculation (EGR) valve - component in the EGR system, used to meter a controlled amount of exhaust gas into the intake air stream.

exhaust manifold - the part of the exhaust system that is fastened to the cylinder head.

exhaust pipe - the pipe between the exhaust manifold and muffler.

exhaust port - the passage or opening in a four stroke cylinder head for the exhaust valve.

exhaust stroke - the final stroke in a 4-stroke cycle engine during which the exhaust valve is open and the intake valve is closed, exhausting the combusted gases.

exhaust valves - poppet valves in the cylinder head that control the flow of exhaust from the engine.

expansion - to make greater in size; in mechanical terms, the expanding in volume of gas in a cylinder of an internal combustion engine after explosion.

--f--

Fahrenheit - a scale of temperature measurement with the boiling point of water at 212°F and the freezing point at 32°F.

fan - a mechanically or electrically driven propeller that draws or pushes air through the radiator, condenser, heater core or evaporator core.

fan clutch - a device attached to a mechanically driven cooling fan that allows the fan to freewheel when the engine is cold or the vehicle is driven at speed.

fan shroud - an enclosure that routes air through the radiator cooling fins.

feedback - a basic concept in the way the engine control system works. 'Feedback' refers to the mechanism whereby the computer is able to measure the oxygen in the exhaust stream and then modify the amount of fuel injected into the intake manifold, to optimize exhaust emissions by keeping the air/fuel ratio at stoichiometry.

feeler gauge - thin metal strip manufactured in precise thickness and used to measure clearance between parts; usually part of a set.

field coil - a wire coil on an alternator rotor or starter motor frame; a field coil produces a magnetic field when energized.

filter - a screen or filter element that can be made to filter specified sizes of particles from air or liquid.

flooding - a condition in which unvaporized fuel in the intake manifold and/or combustion area prevents the engine from starting.

flutter - as applied to engine valves, refers to a condition wherein the valve is not held tightly on its seat due to a weak valve spring, during the time the cam is not lifting it.

flux density - the degree of concentration of the magnetic lines of force that emanate from a magnetic sensor; when the tooth of a reluctor aligns with the sensor tip, the magnetic lines of force are squeezed together, which increases flux density.

foot pound - a unit of measurement for torque. One foot pound is the torque obtained by a force of one pound applied to a wrench handle that is 12-in. long; a unit of energy required to raise a weight of one pound, a distance of one foot.

force - a pushing effort measured in pounds; the form of energy that puts an object at rest into motion or changes the motion of a moving object.

four stroke cycle engine - an engine, either gasoline or diesel that uses four strokes: intake, compression, power and exhaust. A firing impulse occurs every two turns of the crankshaft. When this engine is a gasoline engine it is also called an Otto cycle engine after its inventor. A diesel engine is called a Diesel cycle engine for the same reason.

freeze frame - parameters of engine/powertrain operating conditions stored in PCM memory the instant a DTC is set in an OBD II system.

frequency - the number of cycles of a periodic waveform typically measured in one second intervals or hertz (cycles per second).

friction - resistance to motion that occurs when two objects rub against each other.

fuel injection - a system that sprays fuel directly into the intake air stream.

fuel injector - an electrically-opened nozzle that sprays finely atomized fuel through its aperture into the intake manifold during a cylinder's intake stroke. On some vehicles, these injections are sequential, on others, the injectors are fired all at once or in banks.

fuel pressure regulator - uses intake manifold vacuum, or more properly intake manifold absolute pressure (MAP), to modify the pressure in the fuel rail. The fuel pump can pump more fuel than the engine can use, so the system routes the extra fuel back to the tank through the fuel pressure regulator.

fuel pump - a mechanical or electronic device that draws fuel from the fuel tank and sends it to the carburetor or fuel injection system.

fuel pump (FP) relay - the computer controls the electric fuel pump by energizing the fuel pump relay. It does so by grounding the fuel pump relay coil circuit. The relay then directly supplies power to the fuel pump.

fuel rail - a manifold used to connect fuel injectors to the fuel pump.

fuel shutoff - works by de-energizing the fuel pump relay. This occurs if the engine speed sensor indicates excessive engine speed or if the vehicle speed sensor indicates a certain mph.

fuel trim (STFT/LTFT) - fuel delivery (volume) adjustments based on closed loop feedback. Values above the nominal value (0%) indicate increased injector pulse width (IPW); values below 0% indicate decreased injector pulse width. Positive percentages indicate richening air/fuel ratio; negative percentages indicate a leaning air/fuel ratio. Short Term Fuel Trim (STFT) is based on current oxygen sensor switching values. Long Term Fuel Trim (LTFT) is a learned value used to compensate for continual deviation of STFT from the nominal value. For example, if STFT continually signals richening the air/fuel ratio, it will reach a value sufficient to increment the LTFT to a richer value.

fuel, ignition or spark map - a multi-dimensional 'map' that correlates engine speed, temperature, load and other factors into a specific spark advance and fuel injection pulse width for that set of conditions. There are several such 'maps' in the computer's hard-wired memory. The fine-tuning of the fuel mixture is completed by the signal from the oxygen sensor. On some vehicles, a knock sensor is included to fine-tune the ignition advance to accommodate differences in fuel octane rating and engine wear.

fuse - a metal circuit protection device that melts when there is a circuit overload or short.

fusible link - a smaller gauge wire that is included in an electrical circuit to provide circuit protection. The smaller gauge wire will melt when the circuit is overloaded.

--g--

gassing - hydrogen gas bubbles that rise from the battery electrolyte during charging.

generator - a device that converts mechanical energy into electrical energy; SAE J1930 nomenclature for an alternator; a generating device that uses diode rectifiers to convert AC to DC.

ground - a connecting body whose electrical potential is zero, to which an electrical circuit can be connected.

ground circuit - that part of the circuit that is connected electrically to the negative terminal of the battery. Every electric circuit has a power and ground side. Most computer actuations consist of completing the ground side of an actuator's circuit; this protects the computer from short circuits. Resistance in a ground circuit will reduce the current through it and cause deterioration in the function of the circuit.

Glossary of Terms

Hall effect - when current flows through a thin wafer of semiconductor material, and a magnetic field crosses it at a right angle, a voltage known as a Hall effect voltage will be generated at the edge of the material. Interrupting the magnetic field turns off the voltage. This is the principle used by Hall effect sensors.

HC - see hydrocarbons.

heated oxygen sensor (HO2S) - an oxygen sensor with a resistance element built into it to shorten the time needed to bring the sensor to operating temperature. Heated oxygen sensors will keep the sensor at operating temperature during idle, low speeds, and in very cold weather.

heat range - the measure of a spark plug's ability to dissipate heat from its firing end.

heat sink - part of a system designed to be at a lower temperature than its surroundings, used to dissipate heat from that system; device to dissipate heat and protect parts.

heel - the outside or larger part of a gear tooth; the bottom of the cam lobe's base circle.

Hg - the chemical symbol for the element mercury. Engine vacuum is measured in inches of mercury or in/Hg.

high tension - that part of a system that operates under or carries high voltage; in an ignition system, voltages in the secondary circuit of the system as opposed to the low, primary circuit voltage.

HO2S - see heated oxygen sensor.

hydraulic valve lifter - an automatic lash adjusting device that provides a rigid connection between the camshaft and valve, while absorbing the shock of motion. A hydraulic valve lifter differs from the solid type in that it uses oil to absorb the shock that results from movement of the valvetrain.

hydrocarbons (HC) - solid particles of gasoline present in the exhaust and in crankcase vapors that have not been fully burned.

hydrometer - an instrument used to measure the specific gravity of a solution.

IAC valve - see idle air control valve.

IAT sensor - see intake air temperature sensor.

I/M 240 - loaded mode transient test that measures HC, CO, CO2, NOx, and O2 second-by-second. The gas parameters are in grams per mile (gpm). The vehicle is driven on a dynamometer at various speeds and loads, accelerating and decelerating, for 240 seconds. This test is taken in part from the Federal Test Procedure (FTP) required of OEMs for federal emissions certification.

I/M Tests - Inspection and Maintenance tests. Vehicle exhaust gas emissions test required by state governments. The different types are: (no-load - tests that measure HC emissions in parts per million (PPM) and CO emissions in percentage while the vehicle is in neutral with the engine running at idle and/or 2500 rpm. Sometimes CO2 is measured in percentage as a verification gas; acceleration simulation mode (ASM) - loaded mode tests that measure HC, CO, and NOx emissions while the vehicle is driven on a dynamometer at a fixed speed and load. ASM 5015 is done at 15 mph with a load of 50% of the power needed to accelerate the vehicle from 15 to 65 mph in 15 seconds. ASM 2525 is a test at 25 mph with a load of 25% of the same power.

ICM - see ignition control module.

idle air control (IAC) valve - controls the amount of air allowed to bypass the closed throttle to keep the engine at the proper idle speed. The computer also controls the idle speed of the engine, depending on engine coolant temperature and the number of accessories such as headlights, air conditioning, etc. that are engaged. The idle air control (IAC) valve controls air flow through a throttle bypass passage by means of a stepper motor, an electric motor that can move to a specific location in its travel. Based on the information from its sensors and the parameters in its memory, the computer sends a duty-cycle (percentage of on-time) signal to the IAC valve motor to open or close the bypass to increase or slow the idle speed. This signal can range from zero to 100 percent, and corresponds to the amount of air flow the computer determines is needed. Displayed on the scan tool as counts or percentage.

ignition coil - transforms the low 12-volt battery ignition primary current into the high voltage secondary current that fires the spark in the plugs. The current through the primary coil windings builds up an electromagnetic field around the ferrous core of the coil. When the current is suddenly shut off, the electromagnetic field collapses and generates the high voltage in the secondary windings.

ignition control module (ICM) - the computer does not directly operate the ignition coil, because of the comparatively high voltages and currents involved. Instead, it signals the ignition control module when to fire the spark. The (ICM) has a power transistor that turns on the ignition primary circuit to charge the coil by building an electromagnetic field around the ferrous core, and fires the spark by shutting off the current to the primary circuit, allowing the field to collapse and generate a high voltage spark current in the coil secondary circuit. The ignition control module typically includes additional internal circuits to perform other functions such as calculating dwell. Some modern systems have dwell and timing control in the PCM/ECM regulating the ICM to the duties of an on-off switch for the coil.

ignition switch - a key operated switch located on the steering column, which connects and disconnects power to the ignition and electrical systems.

ignition system - the components that produce the spark to ignite the air/fuel mixture in the combustion chamber.

ignition timing - refers in crankshaft degrees to the position of the piston in the cylinder when the spark occurs.

impedance - the total resistance of an electrical device measured in ohms.

induction - the process by which an electric or magnetic effect is produced in an electrical conductor or magnetic body, when it is exposed to variation of a field of force. Induction is the principle used in an ignition coil to increase voltage.

inertia - the constant moving force applied to carry the crankshaft from one firing stroke to the next; the tendency of a body at rest to remain at rest, or of a body in motion to remain in motion, unless acted on by an outside force.

inertia switch - a device used to shut off a system when disturbed, such as by jarring, tipping or inversion; a switch that automatically shuts off the fuel pump if the vehicle rolls over or is involved in a collision.

injector - a device that receives metered fuel under relatively low pressure and is activated either electrically or mechanically to spray the fuel under relatively high pressure into the engine.

insulated circuit - a circuit that includes all of the high-current cables and connections from the battery to the starter motor.

insulator - a non-conductive material used to insulate wires in an electrical circuit.

intake air temperature (IAT) sensor - works by a negative coefficient thermistor that loses resistance as its temperature goes up (like the engine coolant temperature sensor). When the computer applies its 5-volt reference signal to the sensor, this voltage is reduced through a ground circuit by an amount corresponding to the temperature of the intake air.

intake manifold - a part with runners that connect the fuel system to the intake valve ports.

intake port - the passage or opening in a cylinder head that is closed by the intake valve.

intake stroke - the first stroke of a 4-stroke cycle engine in which the intake valve is open and the exhaust valve is closed, during which the downward motion of the piston draws the fuel/air mixture into the cylinder.

intake valve - also called inlet valve, it closes off the intake port and opens it at the correct time in response to movement from the cam lobe.

integral - made of one piece.

integrated circuit - an electrical circuit containing many interconnected amplifying devices and circuit elements formed on a single body or chip of semiconductor material; diodes, transistors and other electronic components mounted on semiconductor material and able to perform numerous functions.

intercooler - a component on some turbocharged engines used to cool the compressed intake air.

jet - a precisely sized, calibrated hole in a hollow passage through which fuel or air can pass.

keep-alive memory - a series of vehicle battery-powered memory locations in the microcomputer that store information on input failure, identified in normal operations for use in diagnostic routines; adapts some calibration parameters to compensate for changes in the vehicle system.

knock sensor (KS) - a sensor used in the engine control system that detects preignition, detonation and knocking. It contains a piezoelectric crystal that produces an AC voltage under vibration.

--*l*--

lamination - thin layers of soft metal used as the core for a magnetic circuit.

lash - the amount of clearance between components in a geartrain or valvetrain.

lash adjuster - a device for adjusting valve lash or maintaining zero lash in certain types of OHC engines. The lash adjuster is stationary in the cylinder head, with one end of a cam follower mounted on top of it. The other end of the follower acts on the valve stem when the camshaft lobe, which is positioned over the center of the follower, pushes the follower down.

leakdown - the designed discharge within a pressurized body from fully pressurized to non-pressurized, such as within a hydraulic lifter.

lifter - the valvetrain part that rides on the camshaft lobe.

light-emitting diode (LED) - a type of digital electronic display used as either single indicator lights or grouped to show a set of letters or numbers.

liquid crystal diode (LCD) - a type of digital electronic display made of special glass and liquid; requires a separate light source.

load - in mechanics, the amount of work performed by an engine; specifically, the external resistance applied to the engine by the machine it is operating. In electrical terms, the amount of power delivered by a generator, motor, etc., or carried by a circuit. The work an engine must do, under which it operates more slowly and less efficiently (e.g., driving up a hill, pulling extra weight).

lobe - the eccentric part of the camshaft that moves the lifter.

--*m*--

MAF sensor - see mass air flow sensor.

magnet - any substance that attracts iron, steel or any ferrous metal alloy.

magnetic field - the areas surrounding the poles of a magnet that are affected by its forces of attraction or repulsion; the region of space in which there is a measurable magnetic force.

magnetic pulse generator - sensor used to monitor the position of a rotating part such as a crankshaft or input shaft.

malfunction indicator light (MIL) - also known as the CHECK ENGINE or SERVICE ENGINE SOON light on many vehicles. The MIL comes on when the ignition is first turned on (to check the bulb) and then goes out once the engine is started, unless a trouble code is stored in the computer. If the MIL is on when the vehicle is running, there has been a malfunction on one of the sensor or actuator circuits monitored by the computer, and a diagnosis will have to be made by retrieving the code.

manifold absolute pressure - measure of the degree of vacuum or pressure within an intake manifold.

manifold absolute pressure (MAP) sensor - a sensor that measures changes in intake manifold pressure resulting from changes in engine load and speed. The pressure in the intake manifold as referenced to a perfect vacuum. Manifold vacuum is the difference between MAP and atmosphere pressure. For example, in a standard atmosphere (sea level) the pressure is 29.92 inches of mercury, 101 kilopascals, or 0 inches of vacuum.

manifold vacuum - relatively low pressure in an engine's intake manifold just below the throttle plate(s). Manifold vacuum is highest at idle and drops during acceleration.

MAP sensor - see manifold absolute pressure sensor.

mass air flow (MAF) sensor - a sensor in a fuel injection system that measures the mass (weight/density) of the incoming air flowing through a meter. The measurement transmitted to the PCM/ECM is usually either a frequency or a voltage.

mechanical efficiency - ratio between the indicated horsepower and the brake horsepower of any given engine.

memory - part of a computer that stores or holds programs and other data.

meter - an instrument used for measuring, especially the flow of a gas, liquid or electrical charge; to regulate the flow of a gas, liquid or electrical charge; to control the amount of fuel passing into an injector or carburetor.

methanol - a colorless, flammable, highly volatile liquid obtained by the distillation of wood, and synthesized chiefly from carbon monoxide and hydrogen. It is used chiefly as a fuel and a solvent; also known as methyl alcohol; the lightest and simplest of alcohols.

microprocessor - the portion of a microcomputer that receives sensor input and handles calculations.

misfire - failure of an explosion to occur in one or more cylinders while the engine is running; can be continuous or intermittent failure.

miss - a lack of power observed in one or more cylinders, either regularly or intermittently.

module - an electronic control unit.

monolithic substrate - the ceramic honeycomb structure in a catalytic converter that is coated with the catalysts.

multimeter - a tool that combines the functions of a voltmeter, ohmmeter and ammeter into one diagnostic instrument.

multi-port fuel injection (MFI) - a fuel injection system in which there is one fuel injector for each cylinder.

--n--

negative temperature coefficient thermistor - a thermistor that loses electrical resistance as it gets warmer. The temperature sensors for the computer control system are negative temperature coefficient thermistors. The effect is to systematically lower the 5-volt reference voltage sent them by the computer, yielding a signal that corresponds to the temperature of the measured source. Typically the ECT and IAT sensors use this principle.

normally aspirated - the method by which an internal combustion engine draws air into the combustion chamber. As the piston moves downward in the cylinder, it creates a vacuum that draws air into the combustion chamber through the intake manifold.

normal wear - the average expected wear when operating under normal conditions.

NOx - see oxides of nitrogen.

--o--

O2S - see oxygen sensor.

octane - rating indicating a fuel's tendency to resist detonation.

ohm - a unit of electrical resistance of a circuit in which an electromotive force of one volt maintains a current of one ampere, named after German physicist Georg Ohm.

ohmmeter - an instrument that measures electrical resistance in ohms.

Ohm's Law - expresses the relationship between current, resistance and voltage in any electrical circuit. Ohm's law states that the voltage in a circuit is equal to the current multiplied by the resistance.

on-board diagnostics (OBD) - a diagnostic software system in the ECM or PCM that monitors computer inputs, outputs, and resultant engine/transmission operations for failure. OBD I is thought of as any of the systems in use before OBD II, typically 1979 to 1995 systems, although some OEMs started transitioning to OBD II in 1994 and 1995. OBD II has been a federally mandated system since 1996, it monitors emission control systems for degradation as well as for failures.

open circuit - an electrical circuit that has a break, an intentional (switch) or unintentional (bad connection) break in the wire, preventing the flow of electrons.

open loop - the state of the engine control system before it has reached a point when the feedback mechanism from the oxygen sensor is in operation. The fuel mixture is determined by a fixed memory in the computer that correlates specific loads, temperatures, and speeds with specific quantities of fuel to inject.

orifice - a precisely-sized hole that controls the flow of fluid.

oscilloscope - an instrument that displays electrical activity in the form of line patterns on a screen.

oxides of nitrogen (NOx) - various compounds of oxygen and nitrogen that are formed in the cylinders during combustion, and are part of the exhaust gas.

oxygen sensor (O2S) - a sensor that consists of a ceramic zirconium thimble, coated on each side with a very thin film of platinum. Once it reaches operating temperature of 600°F (316°C), the oxygen sensor begins to function as a very low current battery, producing between 0 and 1.0 volt with the output corresponding to the difference in

Glossary of Terms

oxygen between the exhaust and the ambient air. The signal from the oxygen sensor enables the computer to keep the air/fuel mixture as close as possible to the stoichiometric mixture. Under normal conditions, the oxygen sensor signal should fluctuate above and below 450 millivolts several times a second while the system is in closed loop.

--p--

parallel circuit - a circuit with more than one path for the current to follow.

PCM - see powertrain control module.

PCV system - see positive crankcase ventilation system.

PCV valve - a part of the positive crankcase ventilation system. Meters crankcase vapors into the intake manifold.

period - in an electrical signal the period is the amount of time it takes for one cycle of an electrical signal to repeat itself; the number of periods that occur in one second is the frequency of the signal.

pickup coil - a weak, permanent magnet-and-wire assembly that forms a position sensor.

piezoelectric sensor - a sensor that generates voltage from physical shock or motion, a knock sensor.

pintle - the center pin used to control fluid passing through a hole; a small pin or point shaft used to open or close a passageway.

polarity - the particular state (positive or negative) with reference to the two magnetic poles.

port fuel injection - a fuel injection system that uses one injector at each cylinder, making fuel distribution exactly equal among all the cylinders.

ports - valve openings in a cylinder head.

positive crankcase ventilation (PCV) system - a system that controls crankcase emissions by using a valve to meter crankcase vapors into the intake manifold.

potentiometer - a device that changes voltage by varying its internal resistance.

power - the capacity to exert physical force or energy, measured in terms of the rate at which it can be exerted, e.g. - horsepower or watts.

power circuit - the part of the circuit that is connected electrically to the positive terminal of the battery. Every electric circuit has a power and a ground side. On computer controlled systems, ordinarily power is routed to actuators directly through the ignition switch; the circuit is completed when the computer grounds it. Most manual switches directly connect the power side of the circuit to the load. Fuses are ordinarily positioned as close as possible to the battery on the power side of a circuit.

power stroke - the third stroke of a four-stroke cycle engine, which begins with the combustion of the air/fuel mixture, driving the piston away from TDC, which in turn exerts turning force on the crankshaft.

powertrain control module (PCM) - on vehicles with computer control systems, the main computer that determines engine operation based on sensor inputs and by using its actuator outputs. The PCM may also control transmission operation.

preignition - also called ping, it is abnormal combustion of the air/fuel mixture before it is time to do so. A hot surface or carbon deposit in the combustion chamber ignites the air/fuel mixture before the spark plug is fired. The sound of preignition can be heard as the cylinder walls vibrate. Detonation is sometimes confused with preignition.

pressure - the exertion of force upon a body, measured in pounds per square inch on a gauge.

primary circuit - the low-voltage circuit of an ignition system.

printed circuit - an electrical circuit formed by electrically conductive paths printed on a board.

program - a set of instructions or procedures that a computer must follow when controlling a system.

pulse width - the length of time during which a circuit is energized.

pulse width modulated - electronic control of a solenoid that rapidly cycles it on and off many times per second in order to achieve a specific output.

purge - to cleanse or rid of impurities or foreign matter, as in the carrying off of gasoline fumes from the carbon canister.

pushrod - a rod between the lifter and rocker arm. They are sometimes hollow to allow oil distribution to the valves.

radiator - the part of the cooling system that acts as a heat exchanger, transferring heat to atmosphere. It consists of a core and holding tanks connected to the cooling system by hoses.

radiator cap - a device that seals the radiator and maintains a set pressure in the cooling system.

random access memory (RAM) - a type of memory used in a computer to store information temporarily.

ratio - the fixed relation in degrees, number, etc. of two similar things.

read-only memory (ROM) - a type of memory used in microcomputers to store information permanently, as opposed to the temporary storage provided by random-access memory (RAM).

rectifier - a device that changes alternating current (AC) into direct current (DC).

rectify - to change one type of voltage to another.

reference pulse - a voltage signal generated by the crankshaft position sensor (or distributor, or camshaft position sensor - all equivalent components for this purpose). The voltage signal is sent to the computer as a fixed number of degrees BTDC for each cylinder, with the signal for cylinder No. 1 distinguishable from the signal for the others.

reference voltage - the voltage supplied by the system computer to certain sensors. The sensors reduce the voltage by a specific amount, according to their function, and send the signal back to the computer. The computer then uses the reduced voltage signal to interpret the information sent.

relay - an electromagnetic switch that uses low amperage current to control a circuit with high amperage.

reluctor - in an electronic ignition, the trigger wheel mounted on the distributor shaft that triggers the pickup coil, which in turn signals the control module to fire the coil.

residual pressure - remaining or leftover pressure.

resistance - the opposition offered by a substance or body to the passage of electric current through it.

resistor - an electrical device installed in a circuit to lower voltage and current flow.

rheostat - a variable resistor used to control current flow in a circuit.

rocker arm - a pivot lever mounted on a round shaft or a stud. One end of the rocker arm is applied by the pushrod and the other end acts upon the valve stem.

roller lifter - lifters that are equipped with rollers at the bottom that ride on the camshaft lobe, in order to reduce friction.

root causes of failure - a component or system failure, which if not corrected, can cause recurring failures. If the secondary (observed) failure is corrected, but the root cause is not, the secondary failure (the symptom) will recur. For example, if a plugged PCV passage is causing high crankcase pressure and consequent leaks at seals or gaskets, and the seals or gaskets are replaced, the leaks will stop for a while, but unless the root cause (clogged passage) is corrected, the oil leaks will return.

rotor - a component mounted on the shaft of the distributor that transfers voltage from the distributor cap center terminal (coil wire) to the spark plug wire terminals; a cast iron disc mounted on the wheel hub, which is clamped by the caliper and disc brake pads to stop its rotation.

runner - a cast tube on an intake or exhaust manifold used to carry air in or out of the engine.

runout - degree of wobble outside normal plane of rotation.

saturation - point at which current flowing through a coil or wire has built up the maximum magnetic field.

scan tool - microprocessor designed to communicate with a vehicle's on-board computer system to perform diagnostic and troubleshooting functions.

scan tool data - information from the ECM, PCM, or VCM that is displayed on the scan tool. This data includes component and system values on the data stream, DTCs, and on some systems, freeze frame data, system monitors and readiness monitors.

secondary air injection - see air injection reaction (AIR) system.

Glossary of Terms

secondary circuit - the high voltage side of the ignition system, usually above 20,000 volts. The secondary circuit includes the ignition coil, coil wire, distributor cap, rotor, spark plug wires and spark plugs.

self-diagnostics - refers to the way in which the computer in the engine or powertrain control system constantly monitors the state of each of its sensors and actuators. If one of them produces an implausible signal, or no signal at all, the system registers a fault code.

semiconductor - a material that is neither a good conductor of electricity nor a good insulator.

sending unit - a mechanical, electrical, hydraulic or electro-mechanical device that transmits information to a gauge or other receiving unit.

sensor - any mechanism by which the engine control computer can measure some variable on the engine, such as coolant temperature or engine speed. Each sensor works by sending the computer a signal of some sort, a coded electronic message that corresponds to some point on the range of the variable measured by that sensor.

sequential fuel injection (SFI) - a fuel injection system that uses one electronically pulsed fuel injector for each cylinder. The injectors are pulsed in firing-order sequence, ordinarily during the engine's intake stroke for that cylinder.

series circuit - a circuit that has only one path for current to follow.

series-parallel circuit - a circuit that combines series and parallel circuits.

serpentine belt - a flat, ribbed drive belt that makes multiple angles, driving several components.

servo - a device, such as an electric motor or hydraulic piston, which is controlled by an amplified signal from a low power command device.

servomotor - see servo.

shim - thin sheets of material, usually metal, used as spacers to control the distance between parts.

short circuit - a condition that occurs in an electrical circuit when the current bypasses the intended load and takes a path with little or no resistance, such as another circuit or ground.

shunt - an alternate path through which electrical current or fluids may flow.

slip - condition caused when a driving part rotates faster than a driven part.

smog - air pollution created by the reaction of nitrogen oxides to sunlight.

solenoid - a coil of wire that becomes an electromagnet when current flows through it. It then loses its magnetism when the current flow is turned off. The solenoid contains an iron plunger inside the wire coil that is spring loaded to one position. When the solenoid is energized, the plunger moves to the other position.

solid state - an electrical device with no moving parts.

spark knock - engine noise caused by abnormal, uncontrolled combustion due to preignition or detonation.

spark plug - an electrical device that is connected to a high voltage source. The high voltage travels down an electrode inside the spark plug and arcs across an air gap, thereby creating the spark that starts the combustion process in the combustion chamber.

specific gravity - the ratio of the weight or mass of the given volume of a substance to that of an equal volume of another substance, e.g. - water for liquids and solids; air or hydrogen for gases, are used as standards.

speed-density system - a fuel injection system that calculates the amount of air entering the engine by using the MAP sensor signal, engine rpm signal, air temperature, throttle position sensor signal, and volumetric efficiency table (stored in PCM/ECM memory). This system uses no direct measurement of air mass entering the engine, as a MAF sensor would.

splice - to join or unite by weaving, binding, soldering, cementing, etc., usually at the ends of two objects.

square wave/sine wave - voltage fluctuations of different shapes in an electric circuit. The square wave goes immediately from one voltage to the other; the sine wave gradually changes, going through the intervening values. An electromagnetic pulse generator like a wheel speed sensor or a reluctor-type distributor pickup produces a sine wave. Hall Effect sensors, photoelectric switches, and other on-off signal generators produce square waves. For many purposes, square waves are easier for computers to work with, so on many vehicles there are electronic devices to modify sine waves into square waves.

starter - the electric motor that is used to start an engine.

stepper motor - an electric motor that can move to a specific position on its range of travel.

stoichiometric - chemically correct. An air/fuel mixture is considered stoichiometric when it is neither too rich nor too lean; an ideal mixture is composed of 14.7 parts air to one part fuel.

substrate - a part, substance or element that lies beneath and supports another; a ceramic honeycomb grid structure that is coated with catalyst materials.

supercharger - a compressor, mechanically driven by the engine's crankshaft, which pumps air into the intake manifold.

surging - a condition in which the engine speeds up and slows down even when the throttle is held steady.

switch - a device used to open, close or direct the current in an electrical circuit.

--t--

TDC - see top dead center.

technical service bulletin (TSB) - information published by vehicle manufacturers that describe updated service procedures and service procedures that should be used to handle vehicle defects.

thermal efficiency - ratio of work accomplished compared to total quantity of heat contained in fuel. Fuel contains potential energy in the form of heat when burned in the combustion chamber.

thermistor - a temperature sensitive variable resistor in which the resistance decreases as its temperature increases.

thermostat - a device installed in the cooling system that allows the engine to come to operating temperature quickly and then maintain a minimum operating temperature.

three-way catalytic converter (TWC) - a catalytic converter system that reduces exhaust gas emission levels. Usually consists of two beds of catalyst, the upstream bed (reduction bed) reducing NOx emissions to nitrogen and oxygen and the downstream bed (oxidation bed) reducing HC and CO emissions to CO_2, O_2, and H_2O.

throttle body injection (TBI) - also called central fuel injection, it has an intake manifold like that used with a carburetor. One or more fuel injectors are mounted in the throttle body, which resembles a carburetor in physical appearance.

throttle position (TP) sensor - a potentiometer that is mechanically connected to the throttle shaft of the throttle body assembly. It provides an input to the vehicle computer control system regarding throttle position. The TP sensor reduces the 5-volt reference voltage supplied by the computer to an amount corresponding to the degree to which the driver is holding the throttle open.

timing - refers in crankshaft degrees to the position of the piston in the cylinder. When referring to camshaft timing, it is when the valves open. When referring to ignition timing, it is when the spark occurs.

tolerance - a permissible variation between the two extremes of a specification or dimension.

top dead center (TDC) - the position of the crankshaft for a specific cylinder when the piston is at the highest point in its vertical travel.

torque - twisting effort on a shaft or bolt.

TP sensor - see throttle position sensor.

transducer - a device that changes a force into an electrical signal.

transistor - an electronic device produced by joining three sections of semiconductor materials; used as switching or amplifying device.

transmission control module (TCM) - the computer that controls the transmission.

trip - a driving cycle in an OBD II vehicle that allows a diagnostic test (monitor) to run.

TSB - see technical service bulletin.

turbocharger - an exhaust driven pump that compresses intake air and forces it into the combustion chambers at higher than atmospheric pressure. The increased air pressure allows more fuel to be burned and results in increased horsepower being produced.

--v--

vacuum - a pressure lower than atmospheric.

vacuum advance - a distributor mounted mechanism that controls spark advance in response to engine vacuum.

valve lash - the amount of clearance in the valvetrain when the lifter is on the base circle of the camshaft lobe.

valvetrain - parts that convert camshaft movement to valve movement. These include the camshaft, cam timing parts, lifters or cam followers, pushrods, rocker arms, valve and spring.

variable reluctance sensor - a magnetic sensor that generates its own alternating current voltage based on the interference of a moving object across its tip.

variable resistor - a resistor that can be adjusted so the amount of resistance produced in the circuit changes.

vehicle control module (VCM) - same as a PCM with added control circuits for some chassis systems such as traction control, cruise control, etc.

vehicle speed sensor (VSS) - a permanent magnet sensor, usually located on the transmission, which provides an input to the vehicle computer control system regarding vehicle speed.

volt - unit of electromotive force. One volt of electromotive force applied steadily to a conductor of one-ohm resistance produces a current of one ampere.

voltage drop - voltage lost by the passage of electrical current through resistance.

voltage regulator - a device used to control the output of an alternator or generator.

voltmeter - a tool used to measure the voltage available at any point in an electrical system.

VSS - see vehicle speed sensor.

--w--

wastegate - a bypass valve that limits boost produced by a turbocharger.

water pump - device used to circulate coolant through the engine.

watt - a unit of measurement of electrical power. One volt multiplied by one amp equals one watt.

--z--

zirconium - the ceramic material from which the middle section of the oxygen sensor is made. It functions as a solid electrolyte once the oxygen sensor is working (as a battery) to send the exhaust sampling signal back to the computer.

Notes